YANKEE THUNDER

BE SURE YOU'RE RIGHT THEN GO AHEAD.

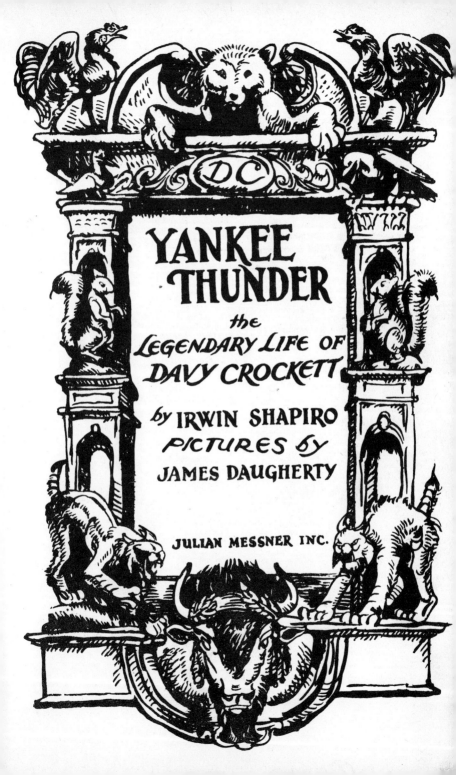

YANKEE THUNDER

the
LEGENDARY LIFE OF
DAVY CROCKETT

by IRWIN SHAPIRO
PICTURES by
JAMES DAUGHERTY

JULIAN MESSNER INC.

PUBLISHED BY JULIAN MESSNER, INC.
8 WEST 40TH STREET, NEW YORK 18

NINTH PRINTING, 1958

CONTENTS

A Note on This Book 6

1. *Strong but Quirky* 13
2. *Frolics and a Taste of Injun* 20
3. *Slickerty Sam* 27
4. *Whittled Down to Man Size* 36
5. *The Ways of the Woods* 43
6. *Death Hug and Mississip* 51
7. *General Old Hickory Andy Jackson* 62
8. *End of the Indian War* 68
9. *The Shooting Match* 74
10. *The Great Tussle* 80
11. *Ben Hardin* 86
12. *Sally Ann Thunder Ann* 93
13. *Dance Her Down* 99
14. *Washington City* 106
15. *The White House Frolic* 112
16. *Slickerty Sam Again* 118
17. *Running for Congress* 124
18. *Trouble from Tennessee* 130
19. *Riding a Twister* 136
20. *The South Seas Trial* 142
21. *Diving for Pearls* 148
22. *The Cape Cod Sea Sarpint* 154
23. *The Big Freeze* 161
24. *Thawing Out* 169
25. *Be Sure You're Right, Then Go Ahead* 177

A NOTE ON THIS BOOK

THE BIOGRAPHER OF DAVY CROCKETT IS immediately confronted with a problem: which Davy Crockett shall he write about? For if there ever was a man of multiple identity, that man was Davy Crockett.

First of all there was—or at least there exists some fairly reliable evidence to that effect—the flesh-and-blood Crockett, the frontiersman and hunter of early Tennessee. There was the historical Crockett, with his heroic exploits at the Alamo duly recorded in history. There was the political Crockett, a figure alternately built up and deflated by the Jacksonites and anti-Jacksonites, according to the exigencies of the moment. And then there was the mythical Crockett, the Crockett of legend and folksay, of the tall tales and fireside yarns and almanac stories—the veritable yaller blossom of the forest, half horse, half alligator, with a little touch of snapping turtle, the ring-tailed roarer who could bring a coon out of a tree, ride a streak of lightning, wade the Mississippi, and come down off the Peak o' Day with a piece of sunrise in his pocket.

It was to this last Crockett, in the grand American tradition of Paul Bunyan, John Henry, Old Stormalong, and Pecos Bill, that I turned as being obviously the most credible, authentic, significant, and true.

Having made the obvious choice, I went to the Crockett almanacs. This series of anonymous pamphlets, published for a period of about fifty years beginning in 1836, justified the title of almanac by carrying a page or so of information on the phases of the moon and similar subjects. The almanacs' real reason for existence was their main text, a collection of tales, anecdotes, and plain and fancy whoppers that had grown up around the name of Davy Crockett. I found them so outrageous, so fantastic, so far-fetched and contrary to the laws of nature, that I knew I was on the trail of the real Crockett.

The trouble was that the tales were too fragmentary for my purpose. Some were coarse, even brutal, and not consonant with the larger outlines of Davy's character. There were glaring discrepancies. We are told, for instance, that as a child Davy was as big as a mountain and weighed over three hundred pounds. But in later life his size is given as no larger than an ordinary man's. There were innumerable omissions, innumerable questions unanswered. How did Davy meet his wife, Sally Ann Thunder Ann Whirlwind? How did he acquire his famous pets, the bear Death Hug and the buffalo Mississip? How did he get to the South Seas and back again? As Constance Rourke has said, "No effort is made to create a consistent mythology in the almanacs."

Faced with a problem within a problem, I had to read

between the lines. I reconstructed, filled in, elaborated. I jumped to some conclusions. I guessed, reckoned, surmised, fabricated, concocted, and wound up with some whoppers of my own. I gathered a little information from books written about Davy and those purportedly written by him. And finally—I confess it with shame—I had to fall back on history.

Let me assure you, however, that even here I did not rely on mere facts. I couldn't. Take Davy's relationship with Andy Jackson. The almanacs say practically nothing about it, and history says they differed on the land question, the Indians, the Bank of America. I knew it went deeper than that, because if Davy is the embodiment of our American democracy, Jackson was its exponent, and Old Hickory is by way of being a folk hero himself. I knew, too, that democracy and its exponents do not always move forward at the same speed. Democracy has a way of outdistancing its most fervent admirers; often it takes some time for us to catch up with forces we ourselves have put into motion. Pondering the hints and half-hints, the shadowy allusions of both history and legend, I caught a glimpse of what had come between Davy and Andy Jackson—the sinister figure of Slickerty Sam Patch Thimblerig Skippoweth Branch.

This Slickerty Sam is a personage rather neglected, as

such, by the historians, but I think they will agree that he left his mark on the American scene. He is a compound of the traditional slyness of the backwoods peddler, the chicanery of the professional gambler, and the brutality of those who seek personal gain at any cost. In him we can recognize the same traits of character possessed by his cousins in Germany, Italy, and Japan, where they have achieved a singular though temporary prominence. That Slickerty Sam has never done so well in this country is a measure of Davy's greatness.

Well, then, I took what I could from history, from the almanacs, from the books. In the end I had to more or less shift for myself, with nothing to guide me but Davy's own motto: *Be sure you're right, then GO AHEAD!* I sat down and put my yarn on paper, writing it for younger readers because I felt they would be less biased against the true and the wonderful, the absurd and sublime story of the real Crockett. I do not claim that mine is the definitive account of his life. All I can say is that I have made a beginning, that in the crazy-quilt patches of the Crockett legend I have begun to discern a basic American pattern—one that in our times, and especially since Pearl Harbor, is assuming a greater importance each day.

For his advice on source material I must thank Dr.

Botkin, consultant on folklore in the Library of Congress, and I must gratefully acknowledge my debt to certain books by the late Constance Rourke and Richard M. Dorson. In Miss Rourke's *American Humor* and in her sober biography of the flesh-and-blood Crockett I first made my acquaintance with the Crockett myth. Mr. Dorson's scholarly compilation of the almanac tales in *Davy Crockett, American Comic Legend,* saved me the task of consulting almanacs other than those in the Library of Congress.

Other books and articles I found helpful were: *The Narrative of the Life of Davy Crockett, Sketches and Eccentricities of Col. Davy Crockett of West Tennessee, An Account of Col. Crockett's Tour to the North and Down East, Col. Crockett's Exploits and Adventures in Texas* (all of these published in the eighteen-thirties, and whose claim of authorship by Crockett is authenticated only for the first); Howard Mumford Jones' preface to Mr. Dorson's book; *The Crockett Myth,* in *Main Currents of American Thought* by Vernon Louis Parrington; *Six Davy Crocketts* by Walter Blair, in the *Southwest Review,* Vol. XXV, P. 445; *The Hero in America* by Victor Wecter; *Hawkers and Walkers in Early America* by Richardson Wright; *The Rise of American Civilization* by the Beards; *A New American History* by W. E.

Woodward; *Davy Crockett* by Frank Murdock, in the *Lost American Plays* series; *Sunrise in My Pocket* by Edwin Justus Mayer; *American Ballads and Folk Songs* by the Lomaxes; *The American Songbag* by Carl Sandburg. A complete listing of the almanacs will be found in Miss Rourke's *Davy Crockett*.

Irwin Shapiro.

New York City

STRONG but QUIRKY

CHAPTER ONE

THE MORNING DAVY CROCKETT WAS BORN
Davy's Pa came busting out of his cabin in Tennessee
alongside the Nola-chucky River. He fired three shots
into the air, gave a whoop, and said, "I've got me a son.
His name is Davy Crockett, and he'll be the greatest
hunter in all creation."

When he said that the sun rose up in the sky like
a ball of fire. The wind howled riproariously. Thunder
boomed, and all the critters and varmints of the forest
let out a moan.

13

Then Davy's Pa went back into the cabin. Little Davy was stretched out in a cradle made of a snapping turtle's shell. There was a pair of elk horns over the top, and over the elk horns was the skin of a wildcat. The cradle was run by water power, and it was rocking away— rockety-whump, rockety-whump.

Now all the Crocketts were big, but Davy was big even for a Crockett. He weighed two hundred pounds, fourteen ounces, and he was as frisky as a wildcat. His Ma and his Aunt Ketinah stood over Davy, trying to get him to sleep.

"Sing somethin' to quiet the boy," said Aunt Ketinah to his Uncle Roarious, who was standing in a corner combing his hair with a rake.

Uncle Roarious opened his mouth and sang a bit of *Over the River to Charley*. That is, it was meant for singing. It sounded worse than a nor'easter howling around a country barn at midnight.

"Hmmm," said Uncle Roarious. He reached for a jug and took him a sip of kerosene oil to loosen up his pipes.

Davy was sitting up in his cradle. He kept his peepers on his uncle, watching him pull at the jug.

"I'll have a sip o' the same," said Davy, as loud as you please.

That kerosene jug slipped right out of Uncle Roarious's hand. Davy's Ma and his Aunt Ketinah let out a shriek.

"Why, the little shaver can talk!" said Davy's Pa.

"We-el," said Davy, talking slow and easy-like, "maybe I don't jabber good enough to make a speech in Congress, but I reckon I got the hang of 'er. It's nothin' to Davy Crockett."

"That's mighty big talk, Son," said Davy's Pa.

"It ought to be," said Davy. "It's comin' from a big man."

And with that he leaped out of his cradle, kicked his heels together, and crowed like a rooster. He flapped his arms and he bellowed, "I'm Davy Crockett, fresh from the backwoods! I'm half horse, half alligator, with a little touch o' snappin' turtle! I can wade the Mississippi, ride a streak o' lightnin', hug a bear too close for comfort, and whip my weight in wildcats! I can out-eat, out-sleep, out-fight, out-shoot, out-run, out-jump, and out-squat any man in these here United States! And I will!"

Aunt Ketinah eyed him as if he was a little bit of a mosquito making a buzz.

"That'll be enough o' your sass," said she, kind of sharp-like. "Now get back into your cradle and behave."

15

"Yes, ma'am," said Davy. He was always polite to the ladies.

"No such thing!" said Uncle Roarious. "Settin' in the cradle won't grow him none! We've got to plant him in the earth and water him with wild buffalo's milk, with boiled corncobs and tobacco leaves mixed in."

"Can't do any harm," said Davy's Ma.

"Might do good," said Davy's Pa.

"Suits me," said Davy. "Let's give 'er a try."

So they took Davy out to Thunder Shower Hill and planted him in the earth. They watered him with wild buffalo's milk, with boiled corncobs and tobacco leaves mixed in. The sun shone on him by day, and the moon beamed down on him by night. The wind cooled him and the rain freshened him. And Davy Crockett began to grow proper.

One morning Davy's Pa got up as usual and looked out the window. Instead of the sun shining, it was like a cloudy night with fog and no moon. Davy's Pa had never seen it so dark in all his born days.

"Hurricane's comin' up," he said to Uncle Roarious, who was standing in a corner buttoning up his cast-iron shirt.

"We'd better water Davy before she breaks," said Uncle Roarious.

Davy's Pa and Uncle Roarious each picked up a

barrel of wild buffalo's milk, with boiled corncobs and tobacco leaves mixed in. Davy's Ma and Aunt Ketinah followed along, carrying another barrel between them.

But when they got outside there wasn't a sign of a hurricane. There wasn't a hurricane coming up, going down, or standing still. There wasn't any hurricane at all. The sky was blue with little white clouds, and the sun was shining just as pretty. Only reason it was so dark was that Davy's shadow was falling over the cabin.

"Davy must have growed some," said Davy's Ma, and they all hurried over to Thunder Shower Hill. Davy was standing on tiptoe with his head poked through a cloud. He was taller than the tallest tree, and a sight friskier.

Uncle Roarious let out a yip and Davy leaned down. Davy wiped a bit of cloud out of his eye and said, "I've been lookin' over the country. She's right pretty, and I think I'm goin' to like 'er."

"You'd better," said Aunt Ketinah, kind of snappy-like. "She's the only one you've got."

"Yes, ma'am!" roared out Davy. His voice was so loud it started an avalanche at Whangdoodle Knob, thirty miles away. The trees all around flattened out, and Aunt Ketinah, Uncle Roarious, and Davy's Ma and Pa fell over from the force of it.

Davy's Pa picked himself up and shook his head.

"He's too big," he said.

"Oh, I don't know," said Uncle Roarious. "He'll settle some."

"No," said Davy's Pa, "he's too big for a hunter. It wouldn't be fair and square."

"What are we goin' to do?" asked Uncle Roarious.

"Only one thing *to* do," said Davy's Pa. "We've got to uproot him and let him grow down to man-size."

So Davy's Ma and Pa, his Aunt Ketinah and his Uncle Roarious uprooted Davy. Soon as his feet were free, Davy leaped high into the air. He kicked his heels together, flapped his arms, and he bellowed, "Look out, all you critters and varmints o' the forest! For here comes Davy Crockett, fresh from the backwoods! I'm half horse, half alligator, with a little touch o' snappin' turtle! I can run faster, jump higher, squat lower, dive deeper, stay under water longer, and come up drier than any man in these here United States! Who-o-o-o-o-p!"

Uncle Roarious listened to Davy and he looked at Davy. Then he said, "He's strong, but he's quirky."

Davy's Pa looked at Davy and he listened to Davy.

"He'll do," he said. "He'll do for a Crockett till a better one comes along."

And when Davy's Pa said that, lightning flashed and thunder boomed. The wind howled riproariously, and all the critters and varmints of the forest let out a moan.

FROLICS and A TASTE of INJUN

CHAPTER TWO

DAVY WASN'T THE KIND TO LET GRASS grow under him.

"Well, folks," he said, "I guess I'll be driftin' along. I'm a hunter, and I'm meant for to roam."

But Davy's Pa wouldn't hear of it. He said it wouldn't be fair and square for Davy to hunt while he was so big. Davy would have to hang around until he was man-size.

Davy gave a laugh and said, "Guess I'm the first two-legged critter that ever had to grow down to man-size instead o' up to it."

While Davy was waiting to grow down, he put in his time being a help to the folks round about. If they wanted to split a rock in two, they called on Davy. All they had to do was swing him up by his hands and heels from a block and tackle. Then they'd push him back and forth, and Davy's head would hit against the rock. The way he made the rocks fly apart was equal to a high-pressure earthquake.

When they wanted to sink some posts in the bed of the river to make a pier, they'd call on Davy again. First they'd lower the posts into the mud. Then they'd say, "All right, Davy!" And Davy would jump down on the posts, hopping from one to the other. He'd make the tallest timbers pop down as though they weren't anything but sticks of kindling wood.

Davy liked being a help to the folks. Still and all, he wasn't satisfied.

"I'm a hunter and I'm meant for to roam," he said.

And Davy's Pa said, "You can't go huntin' till you're man-sized. It wouldn't be fair and square."

"I don't seem to be growin' down none," said Davy.

"Just keep workin' away at 'er," said Davy's Pa. "There ain't nothin' a man can't do if he sets his mind on it."

Davy set his mind on it, but it didn't help. His size didn't come down an inch, and all he could do was wait. He would hardly have known how to pass the time if he hadn't learned how to dance.

Davy was walking down Whangdoodle Knob one night when he heard fiddle music singing out. He was in a hurry to get home, after being a help to folks all day. But the music took hold of him and he just couldn't seem to shake it off. He tried walking away, but he couldn't make his feet behave. Pretty soon he saw it was no use, so he turned and headed up-hill again.

He walked down the trail on the other side, with the music getting louder all the while. At last he came to the place where the music was coming from. In a clearing amid the forest were pitch-pine torches burning, a fiddler fiddling, and some folks dancing a reel. As the folks danced, they sang:

> *I started out from Tennessee,*
> *My old hoss wouldn't pull for me.*

And the fiddler called out, "Now back step and heel and toe!"

The folks back-stepped and sang:

> *He began to fret and slip,*
> *I began to cuss and whip,*
> *Walk jawbone from Tennessee,*
> *Walk jawbone from Tennessee.*

The fiddler called out again, "Now weed corn, kiver 'taters, and double shuffle!"

The folks did the double shuffle and sang:

> *I fed my hoss at the poplar trough,*
> *It made him catch the whoopin' cough,*
> *My old hoss died in Tennessee,*
> *And willed his jawbone here to me.*
> *Walk jawbone from Tennessee,*
> *Walk jawbone from Tennessee.*

A yellow-haired girl dancing by said over her shoulder to Davy, "Why don't you join the frolic, you big ga-lumpus?"

"Yes, ma'am," said Davy, always polite to the ladies. "I ain't never danced before, and might be I'll never dance again! But I aim to dance now, so look out, for I'm goin' to!"

Davy was as good as his word. He joined in the frolic, dancing everything from an earthquake reel to a square-toed double trouble shuffle. The ground shook under his feet, and the folks all said there'd never been another stepper like Davy.

After that wild horses couldn't keep Davy away from a frolic. Once he was walking through the woods when he came upon some Indians dancing on a big flat rock. They didn't have a fiddler, but they did have drums, and a general good time was being had by all.

"A frolic's a frolic," said Davy, and joined right in. His feet started flashing, and he picked up the Indian steps as he went along. Pretty soon he'd danced down all the Indians except the Chief.

The Chief let out a whoop and went into a war dance. Davy whooped back and let loose with a square-toed double trouble shuffle. He stamped so hard and fast the rock began to snap and smoke like a hemlock backlog. In no time at all it burst into fire. Davy kept on until the Chief's feet were singed and the blankets of the others were a-blaze. Davy saw that the Chief had had enough, so he stamped out the fire with a regular grind-the-bottle.

The Indians crowded around Davy, jabbering away in Indian. Davy listened hard, and soon he got the hang of it. Seems that the Indians had never seen anybody like Davy, and they wanted to make him one of the tribe.

"Suits me," said Davy.

So the Indians made Davy one of the tribe, teaching him the war cry and half a dozen Indian tricks. Davy went home with a feather in his hair, jabbering away to himself in Indian. He crept up to the cabin without making a sound, just the way the Indians had shown him. He peeped in the door and saw a stranger sitting near the fire with his Ma and Pa.

"I'll give 'em a little taste o' Injun," said Davy.

Then he burst into the cabin, giving the Indian yell the way he'd been taught. Davy's Ma jumped, and his Pa grabbed his rifle before he saw who it was.

Turned out that the stranger was Davy's Uncle Zebulon, come on a visit from Crab Apple Clearing in Kentucky.

"You ought to be ashamed," said Davy's Ma, "carryin' on that way in front o' your uncle."

"Yes, ma'am," said Davy. But Uncle Zebulon didn't mind. He was captain of the Thunder and Lightning Screamers, the finest regiment in Old Kaintuck, and he kind of liked Davy's way of yelling.

"Don't be too hard on the boy," he told Davy's Ma. "He's a real screamer, and I'm proud to have him in the family." And when Uncle Zebulon left for Old Kaintuck, he said, "Looks to me like Davy will be the greatest hunter that ever was."

SLICKERTY SAM

CHAPTER THREE

WHAT WITH DAVY ATTENDING ALL THE
frolics and helping the folks round about, his name and
fame began to spread far and wide. It spread all through
Tennessee, then over the edge of Tennessee into Kentucky. It spread across the Mississippi to Arkansas, and

27

down the Mississippi to New Orleans. It spread all the way to the Carolinas, and one day it spread to a New England peddler crossing the Great Smoky Mountains into Tennessee.

Now this New England peddler wasn't any ordinary peddler. He had little squinty eyes no bigger than a pig's. When he wasn't talking, his mouth was shut tight as a miser's pocketbook. He had the slyest smile that was ever smiled, and he was bent-backed from carrying his pack.

When this New England peddler heard about Davy, he said, "This here Davy Crockett can't be such a much. Anyway, he won't be when I get through with him."

And off he went, all the way across Tennessee to the Crockett cabin on the Nola-chucky. It was evening when he got there, but he just went up and knocked at the door.

There was nobody home but Davy, so it was Davy who let him in. Davy took one look at him and said, "Well, burn my boots if it ain't a New England peddler!"

Now Davy knew a New England peddler when he saw one. But what he didn't know was that this peddler was Slickerty Sam Patch Thimblerig Skippoweth Branch.

"Nice evenin'," said Slickerty Sam.

"It was up till now," said Davy, who'd heard something about the ways of peddlers. Then he asked, "Got any wooden nutmegs?"

"I might," said Slickerty Sam, and Davy chuckled.

"Got any hams made o' basswood?" asked Davy.

"Like as not," said Slickerty Sam, and Davy laughed out loud.

"Got any white oak cheeses?" asked Davy. "Pocket sawmills? Calico hog troughs?"

"It wouldn't surprise me," said Slickerty Sam, and Davy roared.

Slickerty Sam looked around with his little squinty eyes and smiled his sly little smile.

"Now that we've had our fun," he said, "I'd like to show you my wares. I've got a fine line o' tinware, glassware, brooms, washboards, clothespins, kettles, and pots. All first rate goods, and I give you my word they'll last till they wear out."

"It's pretty late, peddler," said Davy.

"Never too late for a little honest tradin'," said Slickerty Sam.

"If it's *honest* tradin' you're after," said Davy, "you'll show me your goods tomorrow, when we can see 'em by daylight."

Slickerty Sam scratched his chin and thought it over.

"Show me your goods tomorrow," said Davy.

"I can't say *as* I will, and I can't say *but* I will," said Slickerty Sam.

"Tomorrow!" roared Davy.

"Well, all right," said Slickerty Sam. He must have seen he couldn't get around Davy that way, for he said, "But maybe this will suit you better."

He gave a wave of his hands, and the next minute he wasn't a peddler at all. His pack disappeared, and he turned into a tall galoot rigged out in a black slouch hat and a long-tailed coat. He had a gold watch chain across his vest, and a black mustache across his face.

Davy knew right off the peddler had changed himself to a gambling man. But what he didn't know was that this gambling man was Slickerty Sam Patch Thimblerig Skippoweth Branch.

Slickerty Sam walked over to the table. He put down three thimbles, and began slipping a pea from one thimble to the next.

"I never gamble, stranger," said Davy.

Slickerty Sam looked up as though he had been stung by a bee.

"Why, this ain't gamblin'," he said. "I play the thimble game just for the sake o' pastime. I slip the pea from one thimble to the other, and you guess under which one it is. O' course, if you want to make a bet for the fun o' it, it wouldn't be polite for me stop you."

All the while his long fingers were busy, slipping the pea from one thimble to the next.

"Hold on!" yelled Davy, kind of sudden-like. "She's under the middle thimble!"

Slickerty Sam reached out his hand, but Davy knew what he was up to. He knew that once Slickerty Sam touched that thimble, he'd roll out the pea and hide it between his fingers. Then he'd lift up the thimble and show it wasn't there.

Quick as a flash, Davy reached out and picked up the thimble himself. Sure enough, there was the pea.

Slickerty Sam must have seen he couldn't get around Davy that way. He gave another wave of his hands, and the next minute he wasn't a gambling man at all. He was a bully of the river, dressed all in rags and ugly as a mud fence. He was cross-eyed, bushy-haired, lop-sided, knock-kneed, and slue-footed. He had fists as big as

hams, and a face that would have stopped a clock.

Now Davy knew right off that the gambling man had changed himself to a bully of the river. But what he didn't know was that this bully of the river was Slickerty Sam Patch Thimblerig Skippoweth Branch.

"Stand back!" roared Slickerty Sam. "I'm a bully from the Upper Lower Fork o' the Great Little Deep Shallow River! I sleep in my hat, scream through my nose, and sun myself in a thunderstorm! I'm so strong I'm scared o' myself, and I'm growin' stronger every minute!"

"I'll stand back for no man!" roared Davy. "For I'm Davy Crockett, half horse, half alligator, with a little touch o' snappin' turtle! Stand back your own self, before I give you a taste o' my breed!"

"Back up!" said Slickerty Sam. "Back way up! I'd walk ten miles for a fight on a stormy night, and I'm

ready for one now! Back up, before I get hold o' a streak o' chain lightnin' and thrash you with it!"

"Back up your own self!" said Davy. "For I'm the yaller blossom o' the forest, and I'll double you up like a spare shirt!"

At that Slickerty Sam threw back his head and let loose a scream.

"Look out, Davy Crockett!" he said. "I'm the great oak tree that grows half its length underground and turns up its roots unexpected! Look out!"

Davy looked Slickerty Sam up and down.

"You sure *talk* a mean fight," he said. "But I've had enough o' your chin music. Now come on!"

Slickerty Sam must have seen that he couldn't get around Davy that way either. He stuck out his hand and he said, "It was all in fun, Davy. I know better than to fight Davy Crockett."

"Fight or fun, it's all the same to me," said Davy. And he shook Slickerty Sam's hand.

WHITTLED DOWN TO MAN SIZE

CHAPTER FOUR

"NOW THAT WE'VE SHOOK HANDS," SAID Davy, "set down and we'll jaw for a while."

He got out a jug of apple cider and sat down at the table. Slickerty Sam sat down with him, acting as good-natured as a soaped eel. They kept the jug going between them and started to talk.

"That was a mighty neat trick, stranger," said Davy. "Changin' yourself from one thing to another like that."

"Nothin' to it," said Slickerty Sam. "It's just a little

36

trick o' black magic was taught me by my granny, who was a witch in Salem."

And right before Davy's eyes he changed himself to a peddler, then to a gambling man, and back again to a bully of the river.

"The name," said Slickerty Sam, "is Slickerty Sam Patch Thimblerig Skippoweth Branch. I'm a peddler, a gamblin' man, and a bully o' the river. I know three tricks o' black magic, can play any gamblin' game, and I can fight like a wildcat. I'll do anything to get a dollar. I'll buy cheap and sell dear. I'll gamble on cards, dice, or the thimble game. And if you've got a dollar left in your pocket after that, I'll fight you for it. I know a hundred and one ways o' makin' money, and I'm thinkin' up a few more."

Slickerty Sam took a pull at the jug, leaned back in his chair, and talked on.

"Davy," he said, "I'm a mean man. Yes, sir. I'm mean clear through and through, and I'm proud of it. I'll take candy from a baby, cheat widows and orphans, and lie to a preacher. I'm the meanest man in these here United States, and I aim to be the richest."

Slickerty Sam took another pull at the jug. Then he leaned over and jabbed Davy with his finger.

"Looky here, Davy," he said. "We got a mighty big country, but she's goin' to waste."

37

"Goin' to waste?" said Davy, his temper beginning to burn. "There's folks livin' on 'er, ain't there?"

"That's just it," said Slickerty Sam. "That's just exactly it. There's folks livin' here and there's folks livin' there. Folks doin' what they please, and sayin' what they please, and actin' the same. Soon as they get tired livin' in one place, they move to another. And soon as they're tired livin' there, they move again."

"Sounds good to me," said Davy.

But Slickerty Sam shook his head.

"Sounds good, but it ain't good, and it's been worryin' me," he said. "All these folks movin' around and livin' around, and nobody makin' a penny out o' it. That's what I mean when I say the country's goin' to waste."

"What's your scheme, Slickerty Sam?" asked Davy.

"Well," said Slickerty Sam, "my idee is to start small. I'll peddle, and I'll gamble, and I'll fight. I'll pick up as much money as I can, stirrin' up folks against each other so they won't get on to what I'm doin'. And whenever I have the chance, I'll get land. I'll buy it or I'll steal it or I'll get it any which way. But I'll get hold o' all the land I can, and then rent it out for cash money." Slickerty Sam leaned over again and gave Davy another jab with his finger. "Davy," he said, "you're the only man I never got the best of. You and me ought to string along together. The way I figure it, could nobody stop

38

a couple o' men like us. In no time at all we'd own the whole country—lock, stock, and barrel. We could rent 'er out for cash money and live like kings."

When Davy heard that his eyes flashed fire. He banged his fist on the table, and he spoke in a voice like thunder.

"Slickerty Sam," he said, "I've shook your hand, as I'd shake any man's. I've jawed with you and I've passed the jug with you, as I'd do with any man. But now I take it all back. You're no friend o' mine and never will be. You're the meanest critter I ever clapped eyes on, and there ain't room enough for both o' us in the same county. Now stand up and fight, magic tricks and all, for I'm Davy Crockett and I mean to lay you low!"

With that Davy leaped up and cracked his heels together. He flapped his arms, crowed like a rooster, and snarled like a wildcat. And Slickerty Sam began to shake in his boots.

"Now, Davy," he said, trying to laugh it off, "I know you don't mean that. Let's sit down and talk it over peaceable-like."

Then Slickerty Sam shook himself right off the chair and fell on the floor.

"Stand up!" roared Davy. "Stand up, you varmint, so's I can knock you down proper!"

There's no telling what might have happened if Davy's Ma and Pa, his Uncle Roarious and his Aunt

39

Ketinah hadn't come in just then. Davy's Pa took a look around and saw what was going on.

"Hold on, there, Davy!" he said. "You're bigger than him, and it wouldn't be fair and square!"

Davy turned around and said, "Size ain't everything, Pa. He's got magic tricks."

"Don't make any difference," said Davy's Pa. "You're a Crockett, and it wouldn't be fair and square."

While the two of them were talking, Slickerty Sam stopped shaking in his boots. Quick as a wink he skedaddled out the door, and the next minute he'd run out of sight. Davy wanted to run after him, but his Ma said, "Davy! You stay put! You heard what your Pa said!"

"Yes, ma'am," said Davy, always polite to the ladies. All the same, he didn't like it. He didn't like it one little bit.

"I've been waitin' and waitin', and I ain't growed down one inch," he said. "I'm gettin' a mite tired o' it."

"The boy's right," said Davy's Ma.

"What are we goin' to do?" asked Uncle Roarious.

"Only one thing *to* do," said Davy's Pa. "We'll have to whittle him down to man-size."

So the next morning Davy's Pa and his Uncle Roarious got them each an ax, an adze, and a whittling knife. They took Davy outside and began to whittle him down to man-size. They used the ax for the rough work, and

40

the adze and the knife for the fine touches.

Davy was so tough it didn't hurt him any. Once in a while he felt a tickle, especially when Uncle Roarious was smoothing down his funny bone. He gave a squeal and a squirm, but his Pa shut him up with "Stop your sniggerin'. Want the ax to slip?"

When Davy was whittled down to six feet, Davy's Pa said, "I reckon that'll be about right. Six feet seems fair and square."

"Seems so to me," said Uncle Roarious, pulling a sliver of Davy out of his thumb.

They left Davy sitting out in the sun, and went back to the cabin. Together with his Ma and his Aunt Ketinah, they made him a fringed buckskin shirt, buckskin breeches, a pair of moccasins, and a coonskin cap. They put them on Davy, and Davy's Pa gave him a flintlock rifle by the name of Betsy.

Davy took a peep at himself in the Nola-chucky, then leaped high, kicked his heels together, and neighed like a horse. He fired a shot into the air and he bellowed, "Look out, all you critters and varmints o' the forest! Because I'm Davy Crockett, and I'm down to man-size! I'm half horse, half alligator, with a little touch o' snappin' turtle! I can out-eat, out-sleep, out-fight, out-shoot, out-run, out-jump, and out-squat any man in these here United States! And I will!"

And when Davy said that the sun rose up in the sky like a ball of fire. The wind howled riproariously. Thunder boomed, and all the critters and varmints of the forest let out a moan.

The WAY of the WOODS

CHAPTER FIVE

FIRST THING AFTER THAT, DAVY WANTED
to leave home.

"So long, folks," he said. "Now that I'm down to man-
size, I guess I'll be driftin' along. I'm a hunter and I'm
meant for to roam."

Uncle Roarious, he doubled up laughing.

"Why, you don't know any more about huntin' than
a goose knows about rib stockin's," he said.

Davy let Uncle Roarious enjoy his laugh. Then he looked around as though he was standing all alone in the midst of the forest. He pointed to a sweet-gum tree about three-four hundred yards away and said, "See that little twig with a piece chawed off the end?"

"Is there a leaf stickin' up from the twig?" asked Uncle Roarious.

"Is there a little ol' fly settin' on the leaf?" asked Davy.

"Is there a little ol' flea settin' on the little ol' fly?" asked Uncle Roarious.

"Does that flea have a squint in one eye?" asked Davy.

"Which eye?" asked Uncle Roarious.

"The left eye," said Davy.

"That's the very one," said Uncle Roarious.

"Then that's the very twig," said Davy.

"I see 'er," said Uncle Roarious.

Davy blew through the barrel of old Betsy, his flint-lock rifle, to make sure that it was clear. He glanced at the flint, put in a bullet, and filled the powder pan. Then he raised old Betsy, took aim, and pulled the trigger. Bam! and he clipped that leaf right off the twig of the sweet-gum tree. The flea and the fly never did know what happened.

"That's just for practice," said Davy. "Someday I'll show you some real shootin'."

Now all the Crocketts were good shots, but Davy was a good shot even for a Crockett. Uncle Roarious had never seen such shooting before, and neither had Davy's Pa. But they didn't want Davy acting big. All Davy's Pa said was " 'Tain't bad for a beginner." And Uncle Roarious said, "Maybe. But there's more things to huntin' than shootin'. A hunter's got to learn the ways o' the woods."

"I'll learn 'em all," said Davy, "and forty-eleven besides. Won't take me but a little while." He turned to his Pa and asked, "Got any huntin' dogs around?"

Davy's Pa gave a whistle and the dogs came running out, friskier than wildcats. Davy picked out the ones called Whirlwind, Old Rattler, Soundwell, Tiger, Growler, Holdfast, Grim, Deathmaul, and Thunderbolt.

"That'll do me," he said, and walked off into the forest. And right off he started learning the ways of the woods.

He learned the look of the woods in the cool of the morning, and the sound of the little noises by night. He learned the quiet of a still afternoon, and the look of the trees in the moonlight. He learned the riffle of leaves in the wind, the slant of the rain, and the mist curling up from the river at evening. Whatever there was to know about the woods, he knew.

He learned about the critters, too. He learned the way the possum plays dead, and where the rabbit makes his burrow. He learned how a coon goes up a tree, and the way a fox walks without noise on dry leaves. He learned about the deer and the boar, the panther and the weasel. There wasn't a critter or varmint of the forest he didn't know, from the smallest mosquito to the big bear.

Davy didn't forget the birds, either. He learned about the jay bird and the catbird, the blackbird and the hummingbird, the partridge and the wild turkey gobbler. He could whistle sweeter than a clarinet could talk music, and soon he could imitate any bird that ever was. When he wanted to call the dogs, he whistled like a bobwhite, with a little bit of mockingbird thrown in.

Then came the day when Davy figured he was ready to go hunting. He whistled to his dogs and walked to where the woods were thickest. Davy was quiet as an Indian, but the dogs started to raise an awful holler. The next minute a panther came bounding out of the brush. When he saw Davy he thumped his tail on the ground and snarled like a buzz saw going through hard wood.

Davy put a bullet in old Betsy, his flintlock rifle. He glanced at the flint and filled the powder pan with a double charge of powder. Then he looked that panther right in the eye.

46

"Say your prayers!" bellowed Davy. "For I'm Davy Crockett, the yaller blossom o' the forest! I'm the greatest hunter that ever roamed the woods, and this is where I begin! Look out!"

Davy might just as well not said a word, for all the good it did the panther. He crouched back to spring at Davy, yowling something ferocious.

48

Davy raised old Betsy, pulled the trigger, and there was a roar like thunder. The recoil from the double charge of powder sent Davy flying head over heels into the river. Before he splashed a button popped off his shirt and hit a rabbit in the eye.

Davy floated on top of the water, watching what was going on. The bullet hit the panther, knocked him over, and bounced up into the air. It went through a covey of quail, bounced back off a tree, and hit some squirrels standing on the ground. Davy climbed back out of the river and found that his pockets were full of fish.

Davy put the panther on his back, and picked up the quail, the squirrels, and the rabbit. He whistled to his dogs and walked back to his Ma and Pa, his Aunt Ketinah and his Uncle Roarious. When they saw what he had caught they knew it wasn't any use trying to hold him back. Davy was a hunter and he was meant for to roam.

Davy thanked his Ma and Pa for the way they had brought him up. He thanked his Pa and his Uncle Roarious for whittling him down to man-size. He thanked his Ma and his Aunt Ketinah for helping to make him his fringed buckskin shirt, his buckskin breeches, his moccasins, and his coonskin cap. Then he started to say his good-bys.

"Take care o' yourself, Davy," said his Ma, wiping a tear out of her eye.

"Don't you worry about me," said Davy. "I'll be a credit to the name o' Crockett."

Aunt Ketinah and Uncle Roarious were so choked up they couldn't say a word. Davy's Pa was sniffling a bit himself, but he said, "No need to carry on. Davy's a hunter and he's meant for to roam."

Davy nodded his head.

"I just thought me up a motto," he said. "And this is it: *Be sure you're right, then GO AHEAD!*"

"Davy," said his Pa, "are you sure you're right?"

"I am," said Davy.

"Then GO AHEAD!" roared his Pa, whacking Davy a mighty thump on the back.

Davy gave his dogs the bobwhite whistle, with a little mockingbird thrown in. He took one long last look around at the place where he was born, and said one long last good-by to the Crocketts.

"I'd better get goin'," he said, "before I bust out cryin' like a baby."

Davy squatted down low, swung his arms, and made a leap toward the forest. The leap turned out to be higher and faster than he intended. Sparks flashed from him as he flew through the air, and he didn't come to earth for almost thirty-six hours. Some folks thought there was a comet streaking through the air that night, but there wasn't. It was only Davy Crockett, leaving home in a hurry so he wouldn't bust out crying like a baby.

DEATH HUG AND MISSISSIP

CHAPTER SIX

AS SOON AS DAVY'S DOGS HAD CAUGHT UP
with him, he pushed on into the forest. He hadn't gone
very far before he ran spang into a bear.

Now that bear was a smart bear, and he'd learned a
thing or two from the panthers. Instead of running
after Davy, he crouched back and sprang—just like a

51

panther. Davy didn't have time to raise old Betsy or even reach for his hunting knife. All he could do was give the bear a look. It was an almighty fearful look, and it stopped the bear in the middle of his spring. He just stuck in the air above the ground, froze stiff with fright.

The dogs didn't know what to make of it. They sniffed around a bit, then looked up at Davy.

"Guess I'll have to thaw him out," said Davy, laughing at the dogs.

He built a fire under the bear, and the poor critter began to limber up. After a while he thawed out complete and fell to the ground. He stood up on his hind legs, walked over to Davy, and gave him a bear hug. He didn't mean any harm. He was just thankful for being thawed out. Of course it would have crushed any other man but Davy.

Davy didn't have the heart to shoot a bear like that. So he made a pet out of him and gave him the name of Death Hug.

It turned out to be the right idea. Death Hug knew how to behave, and he was mighty fine company. He never did learn how to say anything, but he could grunt smarter than most people can talk. Davy taught him all kinds of things, including how to smoke a pipe. They'd

sit around the fire together puffing away, as peaceful as a couple of parsons.

After that Death Hug kept traveling with Davy no matter where he went. And Davy kept pushing on through the woods, because he was a hunter and meant for to roam.

Walking along one day, Davy came upon a cabin in a clearing. The folks that lived in the cabin crowded up to the door—a Ma, a Pa, and about half a dozen young ones.

"You're Davy Crockett, ain't you?" they said.

"The same," said Davy.

"Welcome, Davy," they said. "We've heard o' you. You're just in time for a bite o' supper."

"That's right kind o' you," said Davy. "But I wouldn't want to cause you no trouble."

"No trouble a-tall," said the folks. "Step right in and set down."

Davy went inside, sat down, and started in jawing with the Pa. They hadn't been jawing long when the young ones set out a ham before him.

"What's the idee?" said the Pa. "Maybe Davy ain't got no taste for ham."

"Oh, I got a taste for it, all right," said Davy. "But I don't want you cuttin' in to a new ham just because o' me."

"We always set out a ham when folks come callin'," said the young ones, giggling and squirming around.

"That's so," said the Pa. "If you got a taste for it, just cut yourself a slice."

"It's a right pretty ham," said Davy.

"Pretty as a picture," said the young ones, giggling again.

"Well, I'll take me a little snippet," said Davy, and he reached for the knife. He started to cut away, but the knife bounced off the ham without making more than a dent.

The young ones let out a laugh and the Pa said, "That ain't no eatin' ham, Davy. It's made o' basswood, painted up to look like what it ain't. We got it from a peddler that come by last week, thinkin' it was real ourselves. Paid good money for it, too, but it ain't worth a thing. The young ones brought it out for a bit o' tomfoolery. Hope you don't mind."

"Don't mind a bit," said Davy, laughing himself. The folks set out real food, and as Davy was eating he asked, "Did that peddler have squinty eyes no bigger than a pig's?"

"That's exactly what he had," said the folks.

"Was his mouth shut tight as a miser's pocketbook?" asked Davy. "And did he smile a sly smile?"

"It was, and he did," said the folks.

"Was he bent-backed from carryin' a pack?" asked Davy.

"Bent almost to the ground," said the folks.

"Then that peddler wasn't anybody else but Slickerty Sam," said Davy. "The same one that's got magic tricks and can change himself into a gamblin' man or a bully o' the river. A varmint like that ought to be run out o' the country. And so help me Hannah, if I ever come across him again, I'll see that he is."

Davy thanked the folks for his supper, whistled to Death Hug and the dogs, and went his way. He kept on hunting, and soon he was the surest shot that ever was. It got so that he didn't even have to shoot at the smaller critters. When he saw a coon up a tree, he'd give it a look and a grin. Sure enough, that coon would tumble right down to the ground. Once a coon up a tree saw Davy walking along with old Betsy over his shoulder. Said the coon, "Don't shoot, Davy! I'll come down!" Seems that Davy's name and fame had spread all over, and he was known to man and beast alike. Sometimes even the wind would rise up and whisper, "Davy Crockett . . . Davy Crockett . . . Davy Crockett. . . ."

Davy began to get pretty tired of it. When he heard about the buffaloes of the western prairie, he made up his mind to have a go at them. He went along to the Mississippi River, waded across, and was all set to push on. But the buffaloes must have heard about him, too, for there was a pair of them waiting on the river bank to meet him.

"Well," said Davy to Death Hug, "there's the welcomin' committee. But where's the brass band?"

Death Hug doubled up laughing, but the buffaloes didn't crack a smile. They snorted blue fire and bellowed small thunder. They stamped on the earth, then began to butt down trees. They played toss with the trees, showing Davy what they'd do to *him*.

Davy let them play. Quicker than a streak of lightning, he slipped around them. He tied their tails together and jumped up on their backs, putting a foot on each.

"Get along, you prairie varmints!" he said. "For I'm a ring-tailed roarer, and this is my day to roar! Now move along!"

The buffaloes moved along, doing everything they could to throw Davy. They raced a hundred miles one way, and a hundred miles back again. They bucked and they heaved, they stamped and they bellowed. But whatever they did, they couldn't throw Davy. At last they stopped with their heads bowed down, as tame as two sheep.

"That'll learn you," said Davy, untying their tails. "Now run along and tell the buffaloes not to fool with a Crockett."

One of the buffaloes ran away as though he'd been jabbed with a pitchfork. The other one hung around, making up to Davy. Davy figured he didn't have any use for a tame buffalo, but he let him stay for a while.

"I guess you're plumb tuckered out, Mississip," he said, naming the buffalo after the river.

Davy had no idea of making a pet out of Mississip.

He might never have done it, if he hadn't found out that Mississip had a fine bass voice. Davy had a good clear tenor himself, and that night around the fire he let loose with a few bars of *Old Dan Tucker*. Davy sang out:

> *Ol' Dan Tucker was a good ol' man,*
> *Washed his face in a fryin' pan,*
> *Combed his hair with a wagon wheel—*

Before he could get out the rest of it, Mississip boomed:

> *And died with the toothache in his heel.*

Then they both came in on the chorus:

> *Thar you go, ol' Dan Tucker,*
> *You're too late to get your supper.*

Death Hug clapped his paws together, and the dogs wagged their tails. Davy kind of liked it himself, so he let Mississip tag along with him.

Davy hunted through the Arkansas country for a while, then went back across the Mississippi to Tennessee. Walking by a place called Frog Bend, he heard singing. Sounded to Davy like a frolic was going on, and of course he couldn't pass it up.

"Guess I'll join in the fun," he said, and went to the cabin where the singing was coming from.

Davy opened the door, and it turned out it wasn't a

59

frolic after all. There was a prayer meeting going on, and the folks were singing hymns.

Davy sat down, with Death Hug and Mississip beside him, and the dogs squatted at his feet. A preacher was preaching, and they all listened respectful.

"We will now sing *Old Hundred*," said the preacher.

Davy let his clear tenor ripple out, and Mississip took

the bass. When they reached the last chorus, the dogs joined in. The dogs couldn't sing the words, but they made a sound like a mighty pipe organ, while Death Hug beat out the time.

If it hadn't been a prayer meeting, the folks would have cheered. The preacher said it was better than any church choir he'd ever heard, and he'd heard the best. He made Davy sing one hymn after another, with Mississip taking the bass, the dogs chiming in, and Death Hug beating out the time.

Just as Davy was getting ready to go, he heard singing from *outside* the cabin. And with the singing he heard horses' hoofs stamping on the ground.

GENERAL OLD HICKORY ANDY JACKSON

CHAPTER SEVEN

DAVY OPENED THE DOOR AND TOOK A look around at who was doing the singing. It wasn't anybody else but his Uncle Zebulon from Kentucky with a troop of Thunder and Lightning Screamers. They were all riding horses, they were all carrying rifles, and they were all singing:

Come all you bold Kentuckians, I'd have you all to know,
That for to fight the enemy we're going for to go.

"Well, saw me into weatherboards if it ain't Uncle Zebulon," said Davy. "What's up, Uncle?"

"Ain't you heard?" said Uncle Zebulon. "General Old Hickory Andy Jackson is fightin' a war and he's callin' for men. Me and my Thunder and Lightning Screamers came all the way from Old Kaintuck to help out."

"Where's he fightin' this here war?" asked Davy.

"Right in Tennessee," said Uncle Zebulon.

"Then thank you, but you and your Thunder and Lightning Screamers can turn around and go home," said Davy. "I never heard o' this General Old Hickory Andy Jackson, but this here is my home state and we don't need any Kentucky men to help out. Davy Crockett will take care o' things in the state o' Tennessee."

"Sure you can handle it?" asked Uncle Zebulon.

"You know my motto," said Davy. "Be sure you're right, then GO AHEAD!"

With that he jumped on the back of Death Hug, whistled to Mississip and the dogs, and roared, "GO AHEAD!"

Death Hug went galloping off like a rough-shod clap of thunder, with Mississip and the dogs streaking along behind. In no time at all they were miles away from the folks of Frog Bend, as well as Uncle Zebulon and his Thunder and Lightning Screamers. Whenever Death Hug slowed down, Davy said, "GO AHEAD! General Old Hickory Andy Jackson is fightin' a war and he's callin' for men! We've got to reach him before sunrise!"

63

And Death Hug streaked ahead, with the dogs and Mississip coming along behind. But after a while they saw a blaze of light shining from between the hills, and they still hadn't reached Andy Jackson. Davy shook his head, and Death Hug grunted, sad-like.

Then that blaze of light began moving toward Davy and he saw it wasn't the sun at all. There was a man moving toward him, and that blaze of light was the red hair on his head. He came closer, and Davy had a good look at him. Just like Davy, he was wearing a fringed buckskin shirt, buckskin breeches, moccasins, and a coonskin cap. His red hair stuck out from under the cap in a cowlick. He had a nose like a hawk's, eyes like an eagle's, and he stood straight and tall as a hickory tree.

Davy knew right off this couldn't be anybody but General Old Hickory Andy Jackson. Davy had never before seen a man like Jackson, and he had to stand back and admire him.

Andy Jackson, he had never seen a man like Davy. And he had to stand back and admire *him*.

While they were standing there admiring each other, there was a rumble of thunder like a roll of drums. Stars flashed in the blue of the sky, and the northern lights rippled out in red and white stripes. Death Hug, Mississip, and the dogs stood at attention, as though the flag was passing by.

At last Andy Jackson said, just like a soldier, "Who goes there?"

And Davy Crockett answered, "Davy Crockett o' the state o' Tennessee."

"I've heard o' you, Davy," said Andy Jackson, "and I'm glad you've come. I'm fightin' a war and I'm callin' for men."

"Glad to be here," said Davy. "My Uncle Zebulon was goin' to bring his Thunder and Lightnin' Screamers from Old Kaintuck, but I figured it was my home state and I could take care o' things."

"You figured what?" asked Andy Jackson, talking slow and looking Davy in the eye.

Davy told him again what he'd figured. And when Andy Jackson heard that, his temper rose up. And when Andy Jackson's temper rose up, he burned inside like a tar kiln. There wasn't a man in these here United States with a temper like Andy Jackson's.

"Why, you Tennessee slangwhanger!" he roared. "You mean to say one man can end this here war?"

"There ain't but one war, is there?" said Davy.

"That's one more than you can handle, you rattlesnake!" yelled Andy Jackson. "Come along with me!"

"I'm comin', General," said Davy, following along to the middle of the woods where Andy Jackson's men were. By this time the sun was really coming up. In

65

the first light of morning Davy saw that the men had had a hard fight. Their clothes were all in rags, and they looked hungry enough to eat a hickory stump. While Davy was standing there, Indian arrows began to fall all around.

"Why didn't you tell me you were fightin' Injuns?" said Davy. "I'm one o' the tribe myself, and I'll end this here war in no time. If I don't, you can tie me up as a dinner for a flock o' wildcats in winter."

With that Davy whistled to his dogs, called out to Mississip and Death Hug, and started off toward the Indians.

"Turnin' traitor, are you?" yelled Andy Jackson. "Come on back, you Tennessee porcupine!"

"I couldn't do that," said Davy over his shoulder. "You know my motto. Be sure you're right, then GO AHEAD!"

When Andy Jackson heard that his temper burned fiercer than ever. It's a wonder the smoke didn't pour out of him on all sides. He threw his cap on the ground and said to his men, "Use your rifles on him! Fire!"

Andy Jackson's men fired, and pretty soon the shot was peppering the woods all around Davy. Then the Indians saw Davy coming and let loose with their bows and arrows. Both sides forgot who they were fighting and began to fight Davy.

With arrows coming one way and bullets coming the other, things looked bad for Davy. He saw it wasn't going to be any hay ride, so he jumped on Death Hug's back.

Those bullets and arrows weren't any comfort to Death Hug, either. So he gave a grunt, crouched low, and leaped high up into a tree. Then he began circling around the forest, swinging from one branch to the next. Mississip and the dogs took to the brush, knowing they could catch up with Davy later.

Away through the trees went Death Hug, with Davy hanging on. They kept on going till Davy sighted Indian rock, that was made of the hardest stone in the world. It was so hard and so high it turned off common ordinary streaks of lightning and made them point down flat as a cow's tail.

"Whoa there, Death Hug!" said Davy. "I guess we'll light right here."

END of the INDIAN WAR

CHAPTER EIGHT

DAVY STOOD ON A SHELF OF THE ROCK AND looked down at the Indians. Sure enough, it was the same tribe he was a member of, Chief and all.

"Hold on, Chief!" said Davy, jabbering away in Indian. But the Chief and the rest of the tribe were so full of fight they didn't stop to see who it was. They just kept yelling like wild critters and letting loose at Davy with their arrows.

Death Hug grunted at Davy, wanting to take to the trees again.

"Takin' to the trees won't end this here Injun war," said Davy. "I'll have to use lightnin'."

Davy rubbed his back against the rock until he felt the electricity rising in him. He struck his left eye with his right hand three times, took a step forward, and said, "Watch out, Death Hug. She's goin' to be a snorter."

Then with a single wink of his eye he let out a hot blasting streak of lightning. There was a noise like thunder, and the rock parted into forty thousand bits, flying through the air in a regular shower. It didn't hurt the Indians any, but it made them listen. When Davy jabbered away again they came crowding around, looking kind of sheepish-like.

"Why, if it ain't Davy Crockett!" they said. "How are you, Davy?"

And the Chief said, "We were too full o' fight to see it was you, Davy. We should have known better."

"No harm done," said Davy. "Now what's this here Injun war all about?"

The Chief told Davy how a peddler had come along and cheated the tribe. Then a gambling man had come along and beat them at the thimble game. And then a bully of the river had come along and started fights with one and all.

"After that," said the Chief, "we figured that a white man couldn't be trusted. We made up our mind to drive away anybody that wasn't one o' the tribe."

"Can't say as I blame you," said Davy. "Still and all, that ain't no way to act. That peddler, that gamblin' man, and that bully o' the river couldn't have been anybody else but Slickerty Sam. He'd cheat anybody, and it ain't fair and square to drive away all the white men because o' him."

Davy went on to tell what he knew about Slickerty Sam. When he was through, the Chief said, "Guess you're right, Davy. Me and the tribe was a bit hasty."

Of course that was the end of the Indian war. The Chief sent one of the tribe over to Andy Jackson to break the news and invite him to a feast. It wasn't long before Andy Jackson and his men came up. There was hand-shaking all around, and Andy Jackson said, "Davy, I'm sorry I let my temper rise up. I'm sorry I said what I said, and I'm sorry I did what I did. You're a ring-tailed roarer if there ever was one. Endin' this here Injun war all by yourself was the neatest bit o' soldierin' I ever did see. I'm goin' to make you a Colonel in the army o' these here United States."

"No need for that, Andy," said Davy.

But Andy Jackson wouldn't listen to him. Then and there he made Davy a Colonel. After that Davy was Colonel Davy Crockett, instead of just plain Davy.

The Indians set up a fine feast, with possum and bear meat for one and all. When they'd finished eating, Andy Jackson said to Davy, "Colonel Crockett, will you take a little turn with me through the woods? There's something I'd like to talk to you about."

Davy answered, "Don't mind if I do, General Jackson. Walk and talk ahead."

So Davy and Andy Jackson went out walking and talking in the woods. By now the sun was high up, and when Davy and Andy Jackson went walking it burned brighter than ever. But it didn't get too hot, for a cooling wind blew through the trees. The birds piped their prettiest, twittering sweet music. The critters went around on tiptoe so as not to make a noise. The trees arched their branches, showing off their leaves. The flowers opened up their buds. And all because never before had two such men as Davy Crockett and Andy Jackson walked out together in the woods of Tennessee.

Davy sniffed the sweet air and smiled to see how nice the day had grown.

"Take my eyes for green grog bottles," he said, "if this ain't the finest country that ever was."

"That's just exactly what I was thinkin'," said Andy

71

Jackson. "And that leads up to what I wanted to say."

"Talk away," said Davy. "I'm listenin' to every word."

Andy Jackson went walking ahead, taking big steps, and Davy walked beside him. After a little while Andy Jackson said, "Well, Davy, this is what I wanted to talk about. We'll soon be needin' a new president for these here United States, and we'll be needin' the best man we can get. I've heard about you, and now I've seen you, and I think you're the man for the job."

"Thank you, Andy," said Davy. "It's nice o' you to say so, but bein' president ain't my line. I'm a hunter and I'm meant for to roam. But if I ever saw a man that was meant to live in the White House, that man is you."

"Thank you for sayin' so," said Andy Jackson. "But I can't see eye to eye with you. The way I figure it, you're the man for the office."

"No such thing, Andy," said Davy. "Why, burn my boots if you just wasn't made to be president—no question about it a-tall."

"Looky here, Davy," said Andy Jackson, his temper beginning to rise. "Do you mean to tell me you won't do your duty and run for president?"

" 'Tain't mine," said Davy. "It's yours."

When Andy Jackson heard that, his temper really burned. He stopped walking and looked Davy in the eye.

"Why, you backwoods hornswoggler!" he roared. "You're the stubbornest critter in all creation!"

"Exceptin' you, Andy Jackson," said Davy, looking him right back in the eye.

For a minute Davy and Andy Jackson stood there looking at each other. The sun burned low, and the birds stopped their music. A mean wind moaned through the trees, and the critters howled.

Then Andy Jackson said, "Maybe you won't say you're the man to be president. Maybe you won't say it's your duty to run for president. But will you or won't you say that we're the two best men for it in these here United States—and it's up to one o' us to take the office."

"There's somethin' in that," said Davy. "You're the best man I ever clapped eyes on, and o' course I'm Davy Crockett."

"Then by the great horn spoon," roared Andy Jackson, "let's find out which one o' us is the best o' the two! And that man will run for president!"

"Suits me," said Davy.

And once again the sun burned bright, and the birds twittered sweet music. The wind blew cool, the trees arched their branches, and the flowers opened their buds. And all the critters walked on tiptoe, not making the least bit of noise.

THE SHOOTING MATCH

CHAPTER NINE

ANDY JACKSON'S TEMPER WAS STILL BURN-
ing, but he was holding it back.

"All right, Davy Crockett," he said. "We'll start off
with a shootin' match. The man that loses drops out,
and the other has got to run for president."

"Looky here, Andy," said Davy. "The way I figure it,
I wasn't cut out to be president, because I'm a hunter
and meant for to roam. But if there's anything I'm good
at, that's shootin'. And if you think I'm goin' to hold

back, you've got another think comin'. I'm Davy Crockett and I hold back for no man—not even for General Old Hickory Andy Jackson. It's a shootin' match you're askin' for, and I'm goin' to slam-bang away. Now let's GO AHEAD!"

"Why, you backwoods bullfrog!" roared Andy Jackson, letting his temper rise again. "We're shootin' for the good o' the country, and the man that holds back is a traitor. But if you think you're goin' to walk away with this shootin' match, you'd better think again, because I'm pretty handy with the rifle myself, if I do say so! Now slam-bang away!"

"You first, General Jackson," said Davy, acting awful polite.

"After you, Colonel Crockett," said Andy Jackson, acting as polite as Davy.

"I wouldn't think o' it, General," said Davy.

"No need to think, Colonel," said Andy Jackson. "Just pick your target and shoot."

"Very well, General," said Davy, giving Andy Jackson a little bow.

Davy turned his right eye three or four times around in its socket to make it see clear. He blew through the barrel of old Betsy, his flintlock rifle, to make sure that *it* was clear. He glanced at the flint, put in a bullet, and filled the powder pan with powder. Then he raised old

Betsy and pulled the trigger, aiming at a little sapling three-four hundred yards away.

But a little bit of a mosquito happened to be sitting on one side of the sapling. The bullet hit the mosquito's leg and glanced off.

Davy's face showed he didn't like it. But all he said was, "Will you try 'er, General?"

"Don't mind if I do, Colonel," said Andy Jackson.

Andy Jackson braced his feet against the ground. He put a bullet in his rifle and filled the powder pan with powder. He took one long look at the rifle, and one long look at the sapling. Then he raised his rifle, aimed, and pulled the trigger.

But a caterpillar happened to be crawling up one side of the sapling. The bullet skinned the caterpillar and glanced off.

Once again Andy Jackson's temper began to rise, and once again he held it back.

"Will you try 'er again, Colonel Crockett?" he said.

"Your turn to shoot first, General," said Davy.

"Just as you please, Colonel," said Andy Jackson.

Andy Jackson raised his rifle again, took aim, and fired. This time his bullet hit where it was supposed to. The sapling split in two, with a crack right down its middle.

"Your turn," said Andy Jackson, stepping aside.

Davy turned his eye around to make it see clear. He blew through the barrel of old Betsy to make *it* clear. He put in a bullet, filled the powder pan, and raised old Betsy to his shoulder. He fired, and his bullet went through the crack in the sapling, just where Andy Jackson's bullet had hit. The crack widened and the two pieces of the sapling fell to the ground.

"Well, I guess nobody drops out yet," said Andy Jackson. "What do you say we try somethin' harder?"

"Suits me," said Davy. "How about snuffin' the candle?"

"That's a good idee," said Andy Jackson.

Davy had a piece of candle in his pocket, and now he lit it and set it up on a stump. The idea was to shoot off the burnt part of the wick and still not put out the flame. The sun went behind a cloud so that they could see the flame better, and they started shooting. First Davy took a shot, then Andy Jackson. They shot until there was hardly anything left of the wick, but the flame still burned. And neither one of them had missed the candle once.

"I guess we'd better try somethin' still harder," said Davy. "Shootin' things off each other's heads would be pretty good."

"Sounds all right to me, Davy," said Andy Jackson.

By this time they were both enjoying the shooting so much their tempers had cooled off.

"What'll we shoot at, Andy?" asked Davy.

"Well, we could start off with an apple," said Andy Jackson.

So each of them put an apple on his head and they started shooting. Of course they both hit the apple, so they tried it with a peach and a plum. They finally got down to trying it with a cherry, and they just couldn't seem to miss.

"Looks like neither one o' us is a better shot than the other," said Andy Jackson.

"Not today, anyway," said Davy. "I guess we'd better try somethin' else besides shootin'."

"Let's try runnin'," said Andy Jackson.

That was all right with Davy, so they tried running a race. They ran it three times, and each time they came out even. Then they tried jumping, hopping, and squatting, and they came out even on those, too. Davy and Andy Jackson were both laughing and having themselves a general good time. But they weren't any closer to deciding which one would run for president than they'd been when they started.

"It looks like we're gettin' no place a-tall," said Davy. "But there's one thing we haven't tried."

"Just name it, Davy," said Andy Jackson.

"How about a tussle?" asked Davy.

"That's the best idee yet," said Andy Jackson, taking off his buckskin shirt. Davy did the same, then sang out, "Ready, Andy?"

"Ready, Davy!" said Andy Jackson.

"Then GO AHEAD!" said Davy, jumping into the air and kicking his heels together. He flapped his arms, crowed like a rooster, and he bellowed, "Now look out, Andy Jackson! For I'm Davy Crockett, fresh from the backwoods! I'm half horse, half alligator, with a little touch o' snappin' turtle! I can look a panther to death, raise a steamboat on my back, and whip my weight in wildcats! Look out!"

"Look out your own self!" said Andy Jackson. "For I'm Old Hickory Andy Jackson, and I'm from the backwoods myself! Now shut your mouth before you get your teeth sunburned, because I've had enough o' your chin music! Come on and tussle!"

THE GREAT TUSSLE

CHAPTER TEN

THERE HAVE BEEN TUSSLES BEFORE, AND there have been tussles since. But there never was such a tussle as when Davy Crockett and Andy Jackson tussled in the woods of Tennessee.

Davy came at Andy, and Andy came at Davy, and they went to it. At first they thrashed around so fast they couldn't even be seen. They were both swift as a rabbit and slipperier than an eel, and neither one could get a grip on the other. They started tussling on a little hill, but soon that hill was trampled down as level as an oak plank floor. They tussled a little longer and found they'd stamped out a hole six feet deep.

"Let's get out o' this, Andy," said Davy. "If we don't, we'll be clean through to Chiny before we're finished."

"Guess you're right, Davy," said Andy Jackson.

They reached out their hands, clasped hands, and they both said, "Heave!"

And each of them threw the other clear of the hole and onto the ground. Then they went to it again, trying every known trick of tussling. First Andy would throw Davy, and the next minute Davy would throw Andy. But neither one of them would stay down. They tussled half the day, and they kept right on tussling. At last they tangled themselves up in a knot and couldn't move an inch.

"Let's get out o' this, Davy," said Andy.

"Suits me," said Davy.

When they'd worked their way free, they stopped and looked about. They'd tussled so fierce they'd plowed up all the land for miles around—trees, roots, stumps and all. Turned out later to be the best farming country in the state of Tennessee. But neither one of them had won the tussle, and they still didn't know who was going to run for president of these here United States.

"Well, Davy?" said Andy Jackson.

"Well, Andy?" said Davy.

"We don't seem to be gettin' any place," said Andy Jackson. "No matter what we try, we come out even."

"Can't both o' us be president," said Davy.

"Maybe there's a better man somewheres than you *or* me," said Andy Jackson.

"You heard about one anywheres?" asked Davy.

Andy Jackson shook his head.

"Now that you speak of it," he said, "I ain't."

"No more have I," said Davy.

"I guess we just can't get out of it," said Andy Jackson. "We're the two best men in these here United States, and one o' us has got to run for president."

"What are we goin' to do about it?" said Davy.

"We'll have to think 'er out," said Andy Jackson.

"Then let's think ahead," said Davy. "Because it's a big job bein' president, and we've got to get the best man."

Davy and Andy sat down on a couple of stumps, trying to think what to do. While they were thinking, the sun began to go down, slow and golden. The light all around turned the same color as the blaze of Andy Jackson's hair.

"The only thing I can think of," said Andy Jackson, "is to start all over again. Maybe this time we won't come out even."

"Sounds all right to me," said Davy. "Let's GO AHEAD!"

Davy and Andy Jackson stood up to start all over again. They both picked up their rifles, ready to have another shooting match.

"Can't see anything around here worth shootin' at," said Davy. "Let's walk on a bit."

Andy Jackson nodded his head, and the two of them walked on through the woods. By and by they came to a clearing, with a cabin in the middle of it. A black cat was coming around the corner of the cabin, about three-four hundred yards away.

"Watch this," said Andy Jackson, raising his rifle to his shoulder. He pulled the trigger, and the bullet shaved off the cat's left ear slicker than a razor. Then he gave a laugh and said, "Top that, you backwoods galumpus! We won't be comin' out even this time!"

Davy Crockett just raised old Betsy. He fired and off went the cat's other ear. The cat never did know he'd lost his ears till he tried to scratch them.

"What were you sayin', Andy?" asked Davy, looking as if butter wouldn't melt in his mouth.

Andy Jackson didn't say a word. He looked around till he saw a little runty pig standing near the cabin. Then he aimed his rifle and shot the curlycue off the pig's tail.

" 'Tain't bad," said Davy. "But where I come from, if we can't do a job complete we don't do it at all."

And he fired at the pig, clipping the rest of its tail off neat.

"Hmmm," said Andy Jackson.

Just then the wife of the man who owned the cabin came walking out. She was wearing a comb in her hair, and Andy Jackson pointed to it with a finger.

"Try that for a target, Colonel Crockett," he said, and shot half the comb out of her hair.

Davy raised old Betsy, aiming at the other half of the comb.

"Excuse me, ma'am," he said, always polite to the ladies.

He took aim, put his finger to the trigger, but he didn't shoot. He lowered old Betsy for a minute, then raised it to his shoulder again. Once again he took aim and put his finger to the trigger. And once again he didn't shoot. He dropped old Betsy and he said, "Andy, I can't do it. I was always polite to the ladies, and I just can't bring myself to shoot at a she-male."

"Why, you ain't any more polite to the ladies than I am," said Andy Jackson. "Besides, we ain't shootin' at her. We're shootin' at her comb."

"Can't help it," said Davy. "I just ain't got the heart to shoot."

"You mean to say you *won't* shoot?" said Andy Jackson.

"I mean to say I *can't* shoot," said Davy. "Can't hold old Betsy steady when I'm shootin' at a she-male."

"Then by the twenty-six states and Texas and Oregon," said Andy Jackson, "you've lost the shootin' match! And I'm goin' to run for president o' these here United States!"

"You'd better," said Davy, giving a laugh and thumping Andy Jackson on the back. "I said you was the man for it, and now it's proved."

"Well, I did sort o' have my heart set on it," said Andy Jackson.

"Then GO AHEAD!" said Davy. He waved his coonskin cap, fired a shot into the air, and yelled, "Three cheers for Andy Jackson, the next president o' these here United States!"

Old Hickory Andy Jackson stood straight and tall. He waited for Davy to stop cheering, then said quiet-like, "Thank you, Davy. If I'm elected I'll try to be the best president I can."

And when he said that, stars flashed in the blue of the sky. The northern lights rippled out in red and white stripes, and there was a great rumble of thunder like the roll of drums.

BEN HARDIN

CHAPTER ELEVEN

BRIGHT AND EARLY THE NEXT MORNING,
Davy said good-by to Andy Jackson.

"I'm a hunter and I'm meant for to roam," said Davy.
"And while I'm roamin', I'll be whoopin' it up for Andy
Jackson. You go right ahead and run for president. I'll
see you in Washington City when you're elected."

"I'll be countin' on you to be there, Davy," said Andy Jackson.

"I'll be there, Andy," said Davy, "so you can count on me."

Davy whistled to Mississip, Death Hug, and the dogs. He picked up old Betsy, gave a wave of his hand to Andy Jackson, and started off. He roamed into every nook and corner of Tennessee, crossing over into Arkansas and Kentucky and the Carolinas. And wherever he went, he whooped it up for Andy Jackson. Whenever Davy met a man, he'd leap high into the air, kick his heels together, and bellow, "Wh-o-o-o-o-p! I'm Davy Crockett, fresh from the backwoods! I can wade the Mississippi, leap the Ohio, ride a streak o' lightnin', and whip any man that's not for Andy Jackson!"

Then that man would say, "No need to carry on, Colonel Crockett. No need a-tall, Davy. I was goin' to vote for Andy Jackson right along."

Of course Andy Jackson was elected. Couldn't have happened any other way, with Davy whooping it up for him. Davy figured he'd hang around Tennessee for a while, then make the trip to Washington City to see Andy Jackson take over the job of president.

One day, when it was almost the time for him to set out for Washington City, Davy was walking along the

87

Mississippi River. He was feeling pretty chipper, so he sang:

> Met Mr. Catfish comin' down stream,
> Says Mr. Catfish, "What does you mean?"
> Caught Mr. Catfish by the snout,
> And turned Mr. Catfish wrong side out.

Just then a steamboat came down the river. Davy liked the looks of her, and he gave the captain a yell.

"What's the fare for takin' me a piece down the river?" asked Davy.

"How many goin'?" the captain asked back, stopping the boat.

"Just me," said Davy, "my dogs, and my pet bear and tame buffalo."

"I'll carry men and I'll carry dogs," said the captain. "But I ain't never carried bears or buffaloes, and I don't aim to start now. 'Tain't natural."

"That's no way to talk about my critters," said Davy. "And if you don't take them, you don't take me."

"Then paddle down the river your own self!" hollered the captain, giving the signal for the boat to go ahead.

"That's a good idee, captain," said Davy as the boat went puffing away.

Davy walked back a little on shore and cut down a hollow oak tree. He hewed one side open with his knife, then corked up both ends. He carried it down to the river, put it on the water, and told Death Hug to hop in.

"Start paddlin'!" said Davy, hopping in himself.

Both of them started paddling, while Death Hug used his tail like a rudder. Away they went, with Mississip and the dogs swimming behind. Davy and Death Hug both lit up their pipes, puffing away like a regular steamboat.

It wasn't long till they caught up with the captain that wouldn't take them.

"Out o' our way, cap!" yelled Davy, and they scooted past slicker than a stream of wind going up a chimney. Only trouble was they paddled so fast the bottom of the log wore out, and they had to take to shore.

Feeling a bit tired after all that paddling, Death Hug curled up on the ground for a nap.

"I could do with a mite o' sleep myself," said Davy. But he didn't curl up on the ground like Death Hug. He stretched out on the water, with a log under his head for a pillow. The dogs and Mississip settled down beside Death Hug, and all was peaceable.

The water rocked Davy like a baby in a cradle.

"I've slept curled up like a snake on the ground, and I've slept in a tree like a bird," said Davy. "But you can't top a river bed for comfort."

No sooner did Davy start to doze, though, than something bumped into him. He awoke in a hurry and opened his eyes—and before him was the queerest contraption he'd ever seen.

First of all, there was a log floating on the water. In the center of the log were three kegs fastened one on the other. And in the topmost keg sat a little fat man, wearing sailcloth trousers, light shoes with ribbons on them, and a snug tarpaulin hat. He had a black leather patch over one eye, and a little pigtail sticking out from his head.

"Well, I'll be shot," said Davy, "if I ever saw a rig like that before."

The little fat man took a good look at him.

"Why," he said, "the critter talks like a man. I thought I had spoke to a catfish."

He had a voice so rough it couldn't be written down, but would have to be shown in a picture.

"Aye," said the little fat man, "I've sailed the seven seas, and many's the sight I seen. I seen porpoises and I seen dolphins. I seen mermaids and whales and sea sarpints. But you're the strangest-lookin' craft I ever come across. Where you cruisin', old rusty bottom?"

Davy didn't like the little fat man turning on him that way.

"Maybe you're new in these parts and ain't to be blamed," said Davy. "But let me tell you, I'm a snorter by birth and education. If you don't go floatin' along and leave me to finish my nap, I'll give you a taste o' my breed, beginnin' with snappin' turtle."

The little fat man roared back, "I'll shiver your mizzen, you landlubber! You copper-bound land shark! You deck sweeper! Just keel over here and I'll show you!"

When Davy heard that he burned like a shovelful of hot coals.

"You old grampus!" he bellowed. "I don't care who you are, you can't talk that way to me! I'm Davy Crockett and—"

At that the little fat man busted out laughing.

"Give us your flipper," he said. "I've heard o' you, Davy, and I wouldn't fight you for all the world. Hurrah for Davy Crockett!"

Of course Davy shook the little fat man's hand, and they became as good friends as a tame hawk and a blind rooster. The little fat man's name was Ben Hardin and he'd seen great times.

"My business is seein'," he said. "I can see more with this black patch on one eye than most men could see with two eyes wide open. Aye, I seen many a thing in my day." He sat back in his barrel and went on talking. "I've sailed the seven seas since I was a little shaver— and the last time I counted I was goin' on ninety-nine years old. I been everything on a ship which a man can be, and many's the time I've leaned my back against a hurricane. Why, I been captain o' ships that turned bottom up in a storm and I had to sail 'em along on their masts."

"What're you doin' around here, Ben?" asked Davy, still floating on top of the water.

"Heard there was a gal in this neck o' the woods by the name o' Sally Ann Thunder Ann Whirlwind," said Ben Hardin. "Heard she'll marry the man that can dance her down, but there ain't never been one could do it. She lives near by, right next to Asphaltum Flats, and that's where I'm bound. Because I've danced gals from Cape Cod to Cadiz right out o' their stockin's, and I aim to do the same with Sally Ann."

SALLY ANN THUNDER ANN

CHAPTER TWELVE

NEXT THING THAT HAPPENED, THEY heard a terrible rumble coming from somewhere.

"What's that?" asked Ben Hardin.

"Must be the echo o' our voices," said Davy. "Don't pay no mind to it."

But the rumble got still louder, and the sky grew black as pitch. There was a blast of lightning, a blow of

wind, and the rain began coming down like a waterfall. The wind blew so strong the trees on the bank walked out by the roots and danced about in a regular forest frolic.

Then the water in the river dashed up in waves six feet high. Ben's craft began to play see-saw, and Davy bobbed up and down. To top it off, the lightning began to blast all about.

"Ahoy, Davy!" hollered Ben Hardin. "I seen storms before, but this Mississippi howler has got 'em all beat. Let's get out o' here!"

" 'Tain't nothin' but a little change o' weather," said Davy. "She'll pass."

"Don't think I care to wait," said Ben Hardin.

"Well, all right," said Davy. "I'll have to leave Death Hug, Mississip and the dogs behind, but I guess they'll catch up with me."

And quick as a wink, he reached out and grabbed a fork of lightning. He leaped up on the lightning and sat astride it, just as if he was riding a horse.

"Comin' along, Ben?" asked Davy.

Ben Hardin didn't wait to be asked twice. He leaped up beside Davy, holding on with both hands to keep from falling off. Davy greased the lightning with some rattlesnake oil he had in a bottle, and away they went. They blasted across the sky so fast the ground below looked like a crazy quilt.

But Ben Hardin's business was seeing and he soon sighted Asphaltum Flats. Close by it was a cabin, so he sang out, "Ahoy! Cabin below! Two points off the port side!"

"Then hang on," said Davy. "And jump when I give the word."

He bore down a little on the lightning and they went sizzling to the ground. There was a flash as the lightning struck, and Davy gave the word to jump.

Turned out that Davy had steered right to the door of Sally Ann's cabin. They let loose a holler, and an old man came hopping out. He had long, spindly legs, a fluff of white whiskers on his chin, and he was carrying a rifle. Davy figured right off this was Sally Ann's Pa, but he hadn't figured on the rifle. Before he could figure any more, Sally Ann's Pa roared, "Who's that raisin' a rumpus in front o' my door? I don't like the idee, and I don't like who's doin' it! Now clear out, because I've got my rifle, and my trigger finger is itchin' to shoot!"

"Then shoot ahead," said Davy. "But that ain't no way to treat a man that's come miles to dance with Sally Ann."

"Oh, it's dancin' you come for," said Sally Ann's Pa. "Why didn't you say so?"

"You never asked," said Davy.

"We're sayin' so now," said Ben Hardin.

Davy and Ben Hardin told Sally Ann's Pa who they were, and he put up his gun. He gave a whoop and called out, "Sally Ann Thunder Ann!"

Sally Ann whooped back, screeching worse than a panther. The next minute she was standing by the door, asking her Pa what was up.

Davy's heart gave a thump and turned over six times, for Sally Ann was the prettiest thing he had ever seen. She had yellow hair smooth as cornsilk and blue eyes like periwinkles. She was tall as a man, frisky as a wildcat, and stronger than either of them.

"Glad to meet you, ma'am," said Davy, always polite to the ladies.

"Will it please you to dance with me?" said Ben Hardin. "For you're as pretty as a dolphin, and I mean to dance you down."

But Sally Ann looked right over his head at Davy, and Davy said, "I wasn't figurin' on it, but now that I'm here I'd like to join the frolic."

"I'm takin' on all comers," said Sally Ann.

"There ain't nobody can dance her down," said Sally Ann's Pa.

"Nobody till now," said Ben Hardin. "Because you're talkin' to the man that's danced the gals from Cape Cod to Cadiz right out o' their stockin's."

Sally Ann kept looking at Davy, and Davy didn't say a word. Sally Ann's Pa got his hemlock fiddle, and still Davy didn't say a word. It wasn't until they'd all walked to the Asphaltum Flats that Davy leaped into the air, kicked his heels together, and said, "Look out, Ben Hardin, you old salt rope! I'm goin' to give you a frolic that'll last you a twenty years' cruise! And look out, Sally Ann Thunder Ann Whirlwind! I'm the man that's goin' to dance you down! For I'm Davy Crockett, the yaller blossom o' the forest! I can out-dance anybody in these here United States, and that goes for present company! Now are you ready, Sally Ann?"

"Ready and rarin' to go!" said Sally Ann.

"Are you ready, Ben Hardin?" said Davy.

"Ready and willin'," said Ben.

"Are you ready with the fiddle?" asked Davy.

"Ready as I'll ever be," said Sally Ann's Pa.

"Then GO AHEAD!" said Davy.

DANCE HER DOWN

CHAPTER THIRTEEN

SALLY ANN'S PA STARTED FIDDLING ON HIS fiddle, and he called out, "Honor your partner and the lady on the left! All join hands and circle to the left!"

Sally Ann's Pa fiddled old tunes, new tunes, and tunes neither old nor new. He fiddled *Old Zip Coon, Money Musk,* and *Pop Goes the Weasel.* He fiddled loud and he fiddled soft, and he fiddled sweeter than honey in a honeycomb. While he fiddled he kept giving the calls, like:

> *The pee-a-wee whistles and the jaybird sings,*
> *Meet your partner with the elbow swing!*

Or he sang out the songs, like:

Coffee grows on white oak trees,
The river flows with brandy, oh!
Choose you two to dance with you,
And swing like 'lasses candy, oh!

And he went on fiddling, playing *Smoky Mountain,*
The Arkansas Traveler, Lonesome Kate, Weevily Wheat,
and *The Devil Among the Tailors.*

The tunes kept coming thick and fast, and Davy, Ben
Hardin, and Sally Ann stamped out the steps likewise.
There never was such dancing as there was that day on
Asphaltum Flats, and there never were such dancers as
Davy, Ben Hardin, and Sally Ann.

"All hands up and circle to the left!" called Sally
Ann's Pa. And they went circling to the left.

"Half around and back again!" called out Sally Ann's
Pa. And they went half around and back again.

Along about the thirty-third tune Ben Hardin began
to grunt like a saw going through a pine knot. After the
ninety-ninth tune, he began to stagger and roll like a
ship in a sea storm. And on the hundred and thirty-third
tune, he just fell over and curled up like an anchor chain.

"Yee-hoo!" yelled Sally Ann's Pa. "You've danced
him down, Sally Ann! Only one more to go!" And he
fiddled tunes faster than a hummingbird's wing.

"That's more like it!" said Davy.

100

He and Sally Ann whirled around so fast they couldn't be seen. They danced till their shadows were long in the sunset, and they danced in the light of the moon. They danced everything from an earthquake reel to a square-toed double trouble shuffle, and they kept right on dancing. But just as the sun was coming up again, Sally Ann missed a step. She slowed up a bit, missed another step, and slowed up some more. She gave a shiver, a sigh, and a groan, and sank down to the ground.

"Davy Crockett, you've danced me down," she said.

Davy danced three times around in a circle, just to show he could go on. Then he danced up to Sally Ann, singing:

> *What makes you look so lonesome,*
> *so lonesome, so lonesome,*
> *What makes you look so lonesome,*
> *I really wish I knew.*
>
> *I believe you want to marry,*
> *to marry, to marry,*
> *I believe you want to marry,*
> *I do, I do, I do.*
>
> **Now choose your dear companion,**
> *companion, companion,*
> **Now choose your dear companion,**
> **One that'll comfort you.**

"I choose you, Davy," said Sally Ann, giggling as though she was being tickled with a hen feather.

"Couldn't choose any other way," said Sally Ann's Pa. "He's the man that danced you down."

Sally Ann let loose a laugh that would have raised the roof, if there'd been a roof.

"Tell you a secret, Pa," she said. "Soon as I laid eyes on Davy, I knew he was the man for me."

Davy let loose a laugh that matched Sally Ann's.

"Tell you another," he said. "Soon as I laid eyes on Sally Ann, I knew she was the wife for me."

"Well, shiver me mizzen!" said Ben Hardin.

"If that don't beat all!" said Sally Ann's Pa.

They all started talking at once about the wedding—how, when, and where. Talking all at once that way, couldn't any of them hear what the others were saying. Then they stopped talking as quick as they'd started. Coming toward them across the Flats was a cloud of dust, moving with the speed of a hurricane. The cloud came closer, and it was Death Hug, Mississip, and the dogs. They were just catching up to Davy.

"Just my dogs, my bear, and my buffalo," said Davy.

"They look like nice-behaved critters," said Sally Ann.

Soon as she said that, Death Hug, Mississip, and the dogs started to move around restless-like. They howled and yowled and growled, acting as if they didn't know how to behave at all.

"Don't know what's got into 'em," said Davy. Then he leaped up in the air, threw his coonskin cap on the ground, and roared, "Well, tie me up as a dinner for a flock o' wildcats in winter! If I ain't gone and forgot somethin' I should have remembered! Death Hug, Mississip, and the dogs remembered, and they were tryin' to let me know."

"What did you forget, Davy?" asked Ben Hardin.

"I told Andy Jackson I'd be in Washington City to see him made president o' these here United States," said Davy. "And if I mean to be there in time, I've got to start now."

104

"Looky here, Davy," said Sally Ann's Pa. "You've got to marry Sally Ann, because you're the man that danced her down."

"Suits me," said Davy. "I wouldn't marry anybody else. Only thing is, we can't have the weddin' till I get back."

"Now, Pa, you stop pickin' on Davy," said Sally Ann to her Pa. "And Davy," she said to Davy, "if you told Andy Jackson you'd be there to see him made president, you got to be there. Well, the quicker you go, the quicker you'll get there. The quicker you get there, the quicker you'll be back. And the quicker you'll be back, the quicker we'll have the weddin'. So GO AHEAD!"

"Yes, ma'am," said Davy, always polite to the ladies.

"Guess I'll go floatin' down the river again," said Ben Hardin. "I'm too tuckered out to do anything else."

Davy took a good look at Sally Ann, with her yellow hair like cornsilk and her eyes blue as periwinkles. Then he hopped on the back of Death Hug, said his goodbys, and started off.

WASHINGTON CITY

CHAPTER FOURTEEN

DAVY KEPT DEATH HUG GOING LIKE A blue streak all the way across Tennessee. Davy didn't stop for frolics or to talk to folks. He just kept going, doing a little hunting to get him his food. One day, though, a panther reared up right in his path.

"Out o' my way, old green-eyes!" roared Davy. "Out o' my way, for I'm Davy Crockett, and I'm headin' for

Washington City to see Andy Jackson made president o' these here United States! Move along now, or I'll give you a taste o' old Betsy!"

That panther wouldn't move an inch. He just stayed there, thumping his tail on the ground and growling. When Davy tried to ride around past him, the panther leaped right into Davy's path again, spoiling for a fight.

Davy raised old Betsy, but instead of shooting he said, "I've got a better idee."

He jumped off Death Hug, and quick as a wink he'd grabbed the panther by the tail. He swung the panther around in the air until the poor critter was so dizzy he didn't know up from down, east from west, or a handsaw from a barn door. Then Davy made the panther say his prayers and give three cheers for Andy Jackson.

"That'll learn you to fool with Davy Crockett," said Davy. "Now out o' my way, and stay out, or I'll twist your tail proper. And keep on cheerin' for Andy Jackson."

The panther gave a cheer and started off, walking as though the ground was shaking underfoot. Death Hug and Mississip busted out laughing, but Davy said, "We got no time to stand here haw-hawin'. Now get along, or we'll never get to Washington City in time."

The next minute they were streaking ahead again. They went over the mountains into the state of Virginia, and on through Virginia to the Potomac River. Standing on the bank of the Potomac, they could see the Capitol building, high above everything else on Capitol Hill. Mississip started singing the bass of *Hail Columbia,* and Davy sang along. The dogs chimed in on the last chorus, while Death Hug stood as though the flag was passing by. Then they waded across the river and were in Washington City itself.

Turned out that Davy wasn't the only one that had come to see Andy Jackson made president. The streets were full of folks, all laughing and crowding each other and talking about Andy Jackson. There were preachers in long-tailed coats, and hunters wearing buckskins like Davy. There were lawyers in broadcloth, farmers in homespun, and boat captains wearing tall silk hats. There were river men and mountain men and men from the prairies—men from all over these here United States. Davy had never seen so many folks, not even in Nashville, Tennessee. Mississip, Death Hug, and the dogs didn't know what to make of it at all.

"Not much elbow room," said Davy. "More folks here than trees in a forest."

A black-whiskered fellow in blue jeans turned around and looked at Davy.

"Why, if it ain't Colonel Crockett!" he said.

The next minute the crowd was raising a cheer for

Davy. Seems his name and fame were known to all.

"Make way for Colonel Crockett!" hollered somebody in the crowd.

"Colonel Crockett can make way for himself!" said Davy. And he walked along with the rest of the folks.

The street was lined with tall trees and it led straight to the Capitol. Near the Capitol steps was a wooden stand for Andy Jackson to speak from, and the folks pushed up close to get a good look. But Davy stayed on the edge of the crowd so he'd have more elbow room.

"Guess we made 'er just in time," he said, as Andy Jackson's carriage rolled up. The carriage was pulled by six white horses, with soldiers marching on all sides and a band of music playing full blast. The door of the carriage opened, and Andy Jackson got out and stepped up to the stand.

Old Hickory Andy Jackson looked just the way he'd looked before. His red hair shone out like a blaze of light. He had a nose like a hawk's, eyes like an eagle's, and he stood straight and tall as a hickory tree. But instead of buckskins and a coonskin cap, he was wearing a long-tailed coat and a beaver hat.

All the folks yelled and clapped, Davy among them. Death Hug and Mississip roared, while the dogs howled their best.

"Hurrah for Andy Jackson!" cheered the crowd.

"Hurrah for Old Hickory! Hurrah for Old Hickory Andy Jackson!"

Then Andy Jackson raised his hand, and there wasn't a sound. The band stopped playing and the folks stopped cheering. There wasn't the buzz of a fly, the chirp of a bird, or even the rustle of wind in the trees. There wasn't any kind of sound at all, because President Old Hickory Andy Jackson was speaking his speech. He told how he'd treat everyone alike, asking no favors and giving none. He told how he'd try to be a good president, running the country the way the folks wanted it run. And when Andy Jackson said that, there was a roll of thunder louder than a thousand drums. Stars flashed in the blue of the sky, and the northern lights rippled out in red and white stripes.

"And now, folks," said Andy Jackson, "there'll be a little frolic at the White House. I'm askin' one and all to come, and I'll be glad to see you there."

The folks let out another cheer, then started out after Andy Jackson's carriage to the White House. When Davy got there, the crowd was worse than ever.

"You'd better wait outside," said Davy to Death Hug, Mississip, and the dogs. "There won't be a bit o' elbow room in the White House and you'd only be in the way."

Davy went inside, looking at the red carpet on the floor, the marble chimney piece, and the cut-glass chandeliers. Folks were everywhere, with waiters moving among them handing out glasses of punch and things to eat.

Davy stood in line to shake hands with Andy Jackson, waiting his turn like anybody else.

"Glad to see you, President Jackson," said Davy.

"Glad to see you, Colonel Crockett," said Andy Jackson.

And after they'd given each other a little bow, Davy turned to walk on.

THE WHITE HOUSE FROLIC

CHAPTER FIFTEEN

"HOLD ON THERE A MINUTE, COLONEL,"
said Andy Jackson.

"Be glad to, President Jackson," said Davy.

Andy Jackson stepped back and looked at Davy. Davy
stepped back himself and looked at Andy Jackson. The
next thing, Andy Jackson cut loose with a regular wildcat screech. Davy came back with a horse neigh, and

they circled round each other, flapping their arms and crowing like roosters. Then they both busted out laughing and thumped each other on the back.

"Why, you ol' slangwhanger!" said Andy Jackson.

"You ol' bushwhacker, you!" said Davy.

"You backwoods galumpus!" said Andy Jackson.

"You screechin' wildcat!" said Davy.

"You ring-tailed roarer!" said Andy Jackson.

"You red-headed alligator!" said Davy.

"You Tennessee terrapin!" said Andy Jackson.

They shook hands again, let out a couple of yips, and went on talking.

"You ol' hornswoggler!" said Andy Jackson. "I knew you'd be around to see me made president, because you told me you would. But how come you didn't stop to see me as soon as you got into town?"

"Didn't have the time," said Davy. "Only got here just before you made your speech. And I can't stay long, neither. I got to get back to Tennessee for a weddin'."

"Who's gettin' married?" asked Andy Jackson.

"I am," said Davy.

"Well, take my nose for a powder horn!" said Andy Jackson. "Davy Crockett gettin' married! We'll have to drink a toast to that." And he gave a wave of his hand to a waiter that was handing out food and drink.

"Yes, sir, Mr. President?" said the waiter.

"A little glass o' punch for me and the Colonel," said Andy Jackson. "And have one yourself."

"Don't mind if I do," said the waiter, handing them each a glass of punch.

"Here's to you and the bride," said Andy Jackson.

"Here's wishin' you all o' the best," said the waiter.

They clinked glasses, drank the punch, and Davy said, "Thank you, Andy. Thank you, waiter."

"Speakin' o' thanks," said Andy Jackson, "it's me that ought to be thankin' you for whoopin' it up for me."

"Nothin' to it," said Davy. "No need to thank me."

"I don't see eye to eye with you on that," said Andy Jackson.

To keep him from talking about it any longer, Davy said, "Nice little place you got here, Andy."

"Oh, it ain't bad," said Andy Jackson. "She's a mite fancy, but she'll do."

By this time the crowd was so great they could hardly hear themselves talk.

"What's that you say?" asked Davy.

"I can't hear you," hollered Andy Jackson.

"I can't hear *you*," bellowed Davy.

"I'd better do somethin' about this," said Andy Jackson. He thought for a minute, then stood up on a chair where everybody could see him.

Before he could say anything, the waiter yelled, "All

right, folks! Stop this here gibble-gabble! President Old Hickory Andy Jackson has a little somethin' to say!"

The folks hushed up so quiet you could have heard a mosquito sneeze.

"You folks enjoyin' yourselves?" asked Andy Jackson.

"Sure are," said the folks.

"Gettin' enough food and drink?" asked Andy Jackson.

"Enough and to spare," said the folks.

"Gettin' plenty o' see-gars?" asked Andy Jackson.

"Plenty for all," said the folks.

"Now it's this way," said Andy Jackson. "I don't want to bust up this here frolic. But I'd like to go off for a spell and have a little jaw with Davy Crockett."

"You go right ahead, Mr. President," said the folks. "Hop to it, Andy."

"Thank you, folks," said Andy Jackson. "You keep on enjoyin' yourselves. I'll be back in a little while."

Soon as the frolic got going again, Andy Jackson took Davy by the arm.

"Come along, Davy," he said. "Now what were we talkin' about?"

"I was sayin' you got a nice little place here," said Davy.

"Well, she ain't as snug as a cabin," said Andy Jackson. "But she'll do."

Andy Jackson took Davy all over the White House. He pointed out the gilded eagles holding up the curtains on the windows, and the floors polished bright as a looking glass. He showed him the hand-painted pictures, the silver tea set, and the dishes rimmed with gold. He even took him outside and showed him the President's garden, where flowers were already in bloom.

Then he opened the door to a little room and said, "Now we'll sit down in here, Davy, and have a quiet little jaw before I go back to the folks."

They hadn't gone more than a step into the room when they stopped. For there was a man sitting in that room, leaning back in an easy chair, with his feet up on a marble-topped table. He was smoking a cigar, drink-

ing punch from a glass, and eating from a plate heaped with food. He was sitting with his back to the door, so Davy and Andy Jackson couldn't see his face. But they did see that he was wearing a slouch hat and acting as if he owned the place.

"Looks like a Congressman," said Andy Jackson, but Davy knew right off he was a gambling man.

Then that gambling man turned around, and he wasn't anybody else but Slickerty Sam Patch Thimblerig Skippoweth Branch.

SLICKERTY SAM AGAIN

CHAPTER SIXTEEN

DAVY WASN'T EVER A MAN TO WASTE time, and he didn't waste time now.

"Slickerty Sam!" he roared. "Stand up, Slickerty Sam, for I'm Davy Crockett, the yaller blossom o' the forest, and we're face to face at last! I said I was goin' to run you clear out o' these here United States, and that's what I aim to do!"

"No need to get yourself so worked up, Colonel Crockett," said Slickerty Sam, blowing out smoke from his cigar.

"Don't tell me what there's no need of!" said Davy. "Get up on your kickers and let's go to it!"

"Whoa up there, Davy!" said Andy Jackson. "I can't have no fightin' in the White House."

"Then I'll fight him outside," said Davy.

"Can't have no fightin' on the White House grounds," said Andy Jackson. "It wouldn't look right."

"Well, I can do without the fightin'," said Davy. "What I really want is to run Slickerty Sam clear out o' these United States."

Andy Jackson shook his head.

"Can't let you do that neither," he said. "It wouldn't be lawful."

"Know who this varmint is?" asked Davy.

"Don't make any difference," said Andy Jackson. "As long as he's a citizen o' the United States."

"Wait'll I tell you," said Davy. "He's Slickerty Sam Patch Thimblerig Skippoweth Branch. He knows tricks o' magic, and can change himself to a peddler, a gamblin' man, or a bully o' the woods. He's the meanest man in these here United States and he aims to be the richest. I know, because he told me so himself."

All the while Slickerty Sam had been listening and

smiling a sly smile. Now he stood up, took off his black slouch hat, and made a bow to Andy Jackson.

"I'm right pleased to meet you, Mr. President," he said. "But things ain't just the way Davy makes 'em out to be."

Davy reared back to spring at Slickerty Sam, but Andy Jackson held out his hand.

"How so?" he said to Slickerty Sam. "Didn't you tell Davy you were the meanest man in these here United States?"

"Oh, I *told* him so," said Slickerty Sam. "But I didn't mean nothin' by it. It was just in fun. And as for tricks o' magic, I gave 'em up long ago. I've clean forgot how to do 'em. Why, I couldn't change myself into anything if I tried."

"Andy," said Davy, "he's lyin'. The low-down weasel couldn't tell a true thing if he tried."

"Not so fast, Davy," said Slickerty Sam. "You got any proof I'm lyin'?"

"Don't need no proof," said Davy. "You're mean, and we both know it."

"Not so fast again, Davy," said Slickerty Sam. "You got any proof I'm mean?"

"How about all the folks you got the best of?" said Davy. "You sold 'em poor goods as a peddler, cheated 'em as a gambler, and fought 'em as a bully o' the river. How about that Injun war you stirred up?"

Slickerty Sam shook his head, looking at Davy as if he was sorry for him.

"There's lots o' peddlers," he said. "There's lots o' gamblin' men. There's lots o' bullies. You got no proof any o' 'em was me. I'm afraid you got no case a-tall, Colonel Crockett, so you may as well cool off."

"No such thing, you slitherin' rattlesnake!" yelled Davy, turning to Andy Jackson. "Andy," he said, "are you goin' to let Slickerty Sam sit here in the White House, or are you goin' to let me run him out?"

"I'd like to oblige you, Davy," said Andy Jackson. "But I said all comers would be welcome to the White House, and I can't go back on my word. And I can't have no fightin', and I can't let you run him out o' these here United States. Because this ain't the backwoods, Davy. This is the capital o' the nation, and everything has got to be done lawful."

"Mighty glad to hear that, Mr. President," said Slickerty Sam. "There's nothin' that's such a comfort to a body as the law. Guess I'll stay on in Washington City for a while. I got a few idees I want to tell you about how the country ought to be run."

When Davy heard that, he almost went up in smoke.

But before he could get a word out, Andy Jackson said, "I'll listen to you, Slickerty Sam, the same as I would to any man. That's what I said in my speech, and I aim to do it."

"I knew you'd see it my way," said Slickerty Sam.

"I don't see it anybody's way," said Andy Jackson. "I don't see anything anyway a-tall, until I've got proof. That's the way a man has got to be when he's president."

Davy couldn't hold himself back any longer. He reared back again, yelling, "I don't want to cross you, Andy! But Slickerty Sam has got somethin' comin' to him, and I'm goin' to see that he gets it!"

"Careful, Davy," said Andy Jackson. "You're not just talkin' to Andy Jackson. You're talkin' to the president o' these here United States."

"President or no president, out o' my way and let me at him!" said Davy.

At that Andy Jackson's temper rose up, and his face got as red as the blaze of his hair. He jumped in front of Davy, stamping on the floor and bellowing worse than a buffalo.

"Get out o' this White House, you backwoods slang-whanger!" he roared. "Get out o' here before I throw you out with my own two hands! I'm the president o' these here United States, and I'm tellin' you to get out!"

Davy looked at Andy Jackson.

"Why, Andy," he said, "you must have got the whole thing mixed up. It's Slickerty Sam you want to throw out, not me."

Andy Jackson's temper rose up fiercer than ever. It's a wonder he didn't burst into a thousand bits. But all he did was say, "Get out o' here, Davy Crockett! Get out fast!"

"All right, Andy," said Davy. "You're askin' me to get out and I'm gettin'. But from now on we're on different sides o' the fence. And we'll keep on bein' that way, until you see eye to eye with me on Slickerty Sam. Good-by, Andy."

And Davy turned around, left the room, and pushed his way through the crowd out of the White House.

RUNNING
FOR CONGRESS

CHAPTER SEVENTEEN

DAVY WENT OVER TO WHERE DEATH HUG,
Mississip, and the dogs were waiting.

"Get along," he said, and started heading back to
Tennessee.

Death Hug, Mississip, and the dogs saw that Davy
was put out about something and wouldn't stand for
any cutting up. They tended to their business, not letting
loose a howl, growl, or yowl all the way. Davy didn't
say a single word himself. He just kept going till he

124

got to the cabin of Sally Ann and her Pa, standing next to Asphaltum Flats.

"Glad to see you, Davy," said Sally Ann.

"Glad to see you, Sally Ann," said Davy.

"Enough o' this jawin'," said Sally Ann's Pa. "What about the weddin'?"

"I said I'd marry Sally Ann," said Davy, "and I ain't changed my mind. But we'll have to put the weddin' off for a while."

Sally Ann's Pa jumped as though he'd been jabbed with a pitchfork.

"Well, tan my hide!" he said. "What's goin' on here? You been to Washington City, ain't you?"

"I been to Washington City," said Davy.

"You seen Andy Jackson made president, didn't you?" said Sally Ann's Pa.

"I did," said Davy.

"Then what's holdin' things up now?" asked Sally Ann's Pa.

"Give Davy a chance to talk," said Sally Ann.

"I'm lettin' him talk," said Sally Ann's Pa.

"Then let him," said Sally Ann.

So Sally Ann's Pa let Davy talk, and he told what had happened in Washington City. He told about Andy Jackson and Slickerty Sam, and when he was through he said, "Somebody has got to take care o' things, or

125

Slickerty Sam will get around Andy, as sure as shootin'. I figure that somebody is me, and the best way to do it is to be Congressman. If I could get a law passed against Slickerty Sam, wouldn't nobody be able to stop me from runnin' him out o' the United States."

"How do you know you'll be elected?" asked Sally Ann's Pa.

"That won't be nothin' for Davy Crockett," said Davy. "And as soon as I take care o' Slickerty Sam I'll be back and we'll have the weddin'."

"Davy," said Sally Ann, "are you sure you're right?"

"I am," said Davy.

"Then GO AHEAD!" said Sally Ann. "You get right out and start whoopin' it up for yourself. You get yourself elected to Congress, and take care o' Slickerty Sam. Then come back and we'll have the weddin'."

"Yes, ma'am," said Davy. He scooted out so fast the wind of it almost blew over Sally Ann's Pa.

"I can't waste no time," said Davy to Death Hug. "Because the quicker I take care o' Slickerty Sam, the quicker I can get back to Sally Ann."

Death Hug grunted to let Davy know it was all right with him, and Mississip and the dogs did the same.

"That's good," said Davy. "Because I aim to do a rip-snortin' job o' whoopin' it up, and I'm startin' now."

First thing Davy did was get himself a little cowhide bag. He wrote down some speeches and put them in the bag, together with the Declaration of Independence and the Constitution of these here United States. He called it his bag of patriotism, saying that was all a Congressman really needed.

"Guess I'd better practice a mite before I do any real whoopin' it up," he said, and hopped up on a tree stump. He flapped his arms, crowed like a rooster, and he bellowed, "Gather round! For I'm Davy Crockett, the yaller blossom o' the forest! I'm half horse, half alligator, with a little touch o' snappin' turtle! I'm a ring-tailed roarer, and this is my day to roar! Gather round!"

In no time at all a pack of critters came out of the woods and crowded around Davy. There were a cougar, a couple of foxes, a wolf, an alligator, quite a few rabbits, some bullfrogs, chickens, and a turkey gobbler or two. Davy opened up his bag of patriotism, reading off the Declaration of Independence and the Constitution of these here United States. Then he went into his speech, with the critters listening right along.

Davy ended up by giving twenty-six cheers for all the states, with half a cheer apiece for Texas and Oregon. All the critters joined in, raising a mighty fine cheer. Davy whistled some tunes, taught them some dance steps, and they had a frolic. When the fun was over there wasn't a critter that didn't back Davy for Congress.

After that Davy whooped it up among the folks, making speeches like a regular whirlwind. The way it turned out, though, he needn't have bothered. Whenever anybody opened his mouth to speak against Davy, the critters would come popping out of the woods. They'd let the speaker speak for a little while, then bullfrogs would start croaking and the chickens would start cackling.

"Cr-r-r-r-o-ck-ck-ck-ck-ett!" they'd say. "Cr-r-r-r-o-ck-ck-ck-ett! Cr-r-r-r-o-ck-ck-ck-ett!"

The other critters would join in, and before long critters and folks alike would be cheering for Davy Crockett.

TROUBLE FROM TENNESSEE

CHAPTER EIGHTEEN

SOON AS DAVY WAS ELECTED HE HEADED for Washington City again. There weren't any crowds when he got there, just folks and Congressmen walking about. As Davy went up Pennsylvania Avenue, he passed Senator Dan'l Webster and Senator John Calhoun.

"Good day, Congressman," said Dan'l Webster.

"Welcome to Washington, Congressman," said John Calhoun.

Davy gave them both a thank you and a how-do. Death Hug and Mississip swelled up so with pride they looked fit to bust.

"None o' that," said Davy. "No sense gettin' too big for your britches just because I'm in Washington City as Congressman from the state o' Tennessee."

Walking up the steps of the Capitol to take his seat in Congress, Davy heard a voice sing out, "Ahoy, Congressman!"

Steps had more Congressmen on them than a stray dog has fleas, so Davy didn't pay any mind.

"Ahoy, Congressman Crockett!" sang out the voice again. And this time Davy turned around.

On the bottom step stood a little fat man with a pigtail and a patch over one eye. It couldn't have been anybody else but Ben Hardin, and that's who it was.

"Why, you sea-goin' shellback!" said Davy. "Where have you been? What're you doin' here?"

"I been cruisin' around," said Ben Hardin. "Heard you'd been made Congressman, so I come up the Potomac River to hear your speech."

"You're just in time," said Davy. "Now we'd best go in, because I wouldn't want to be late to take my seat in Congress."

While they were going up the steps Ben Hardin asked, "How's Sally Ann?"

131

"Never did get to hold the weddin'," said Davy. "Had to run for Congress, then hurry back to Washington City to keep an eye on Andy Jackson and Slickerty Sam. You'll hear about it in my speech."

Davy left old Betsy in the cloakroom, and sent Death Hug, Mississip, and the dogs to wait in the visitors' room. Ben Hardin went up to the gallery, and Davy walked into Congress to take his seat.

Davy waited till Congress got started, then stood up and made his speech. He told how Slickerty Sam wanted to own all of these here United States and rent it out for cash money. He told how Andy Jackson said it wouldn't

be lawful to run him out. And he ended his speech by calling for a law against Slickerty Sam.

After it was all over, the Congressmen crowded around Davy.

"Nice listenin' speech for a beginner," they said. "Every word clear as a bell. But when it comes to the sense o' it, that's a horse o' a different color. There ain't no harm in Slickerty Sam, and no reason to pass a law against him."

"Why, you pot-bellied hornswogglers!" said Davy. "This here Congress ain't no better than Andy Jackson! But let me tell you, I'm Davy Crockett, and I'm goin' to keep at it till somethin's done about Slickerty Sam!"

Only one who sided with Davy was Ben Hardin.

133

Soon as he saw Davy he said, "No two ways about it, Davy. Slickerty Sam ought to be made to walk the plank."

While the two of them were standing there talking, a little old man came scooting in the door.

"Congressman Crockett?" he said.

"You're lookin' right at him," said Davy.

"Letter for Congressman Crockett," said the old man. He shoved the letter into Davy's hand and scooted out again.

"Who's it from?" asked Ben Hardin.

"I'll know better when I read it," said Davy. He unfolded the letter and saw that it said:

Dear Davy,

I am a Tennessee man in trouble and I'm asking you to help. Can't get away to see you, so I'm sending this here letter. I am on the ship *Thunderbolt* along the bank of the Potomac near a clump of oak trees. Come as quick as you can, because my trouble is bad and getting worse every minute.

Signed,

A Tennessee Man

"Shiver me mizzen!" said Ben Hardin. "What's a Tennessee man doin' on board ship?"

"We'll find out when we get there," said Davy. "Because if there's a Tennessee man in trouble, I'm bound to help. Let's GO AHEAD!"

They streaked out the door, but when they got outside they pulled up short. The wind was howling, the rain was splashing down, and the sky was darker than the pocket of a broadcloth coat.

"She's blowin' up for a regular howler," said Ben Hardin.

"Never mind about that," said Davy. "Come along."

By the time they got to the clump of oak trees on the Potomac the storm had blown up full force. The ship was tossing around in the water, looking as if it was anxious to be off.

"I don't like the looks o' this," said Ben Hardin.

"All the more reason for us to hop aboard quick," said Davy, leading the way aboard the ship.

Davy and Ben both let loose a yell, but there wasn't any answer.

"Ahoy, the Tennessee man that's in trouble!" called Ben.

"Can't see a soul," said Davy.

"Let's look below," said Ben Hardin.

There was a hatch open near by, and down they went.

"If there's a Tennessee man about, let him say so!" yelled Davy. "This here is Congressman Crockett, and I've come to help."

"Ahoy, the Tennessee man!" said Ben Hardin.

But the only answer was the shriek of wind and the thunder crashing in the sky.

135

RIDING A TWISTER

CHAPTER NINETEEN

JUST THEN THERE WAS A THUMPING AND a bumping overhead. And with it there was a voice that said, "I hate to be doin' this, Davy. But I been gettin' along fine, and I can't have you around spoilin' it all. Too bad we couldn't have been more friendly-like."

"Slickerty Sam!" roared Davy.

"And he's hammered down the hatch!" said Ben Hardin.

The two of them leaped to the hatch and gave it a shake. Didn't help any, though. That hatch was shut tight and wouldn't budge an inch.

"Tricked and trapped for fair!" said Ben Hardin. "And it ain't only a Tennessee man that's in trouble."

"This ain't no time for mournin'," said Davy. "Let's get hold o' somethin' and pry 'er loose."

They felt around in the dark for a while, but they couldn't lay their hands on a thing. Slickerty Sam had seen to that. So Davy and Ben Hardin leaped to the hatch again, pushing and shoving and pounding away. Trouble was, they were too cramped and hardly had room to work their muscle. To top it off, the ship was tossing like a buckboard wagon on a rocky road.

"Feels like we're movin', Ben," said Davy. "We'd better get out o' here fast."

They pounded and pushed and shoved away again, till there was a crack showing in the hatch. Then Davy gave one great shove and busted through to the deck. Looking around, he couldn't see anything but the waves of the sea with the dark sky over it. Thunder crashed, and lightning was streaking on all sides.

"Don't look like we're anywheres near Washington City," hollered Davy over the wind.

"We ain't," yelled Ben Hardin. "Slickerty Sam must

have set sail, weighed anchor, and jumped ashore. The storm's carried us clear out to sea."

The next minute they heard snorting and growling worse than a herd of buffaloes on a stampede.

"What's that?" said Davy.

"She ain't thunder," said Ben.

"She ain't the wind," said Davy.

"And then again she ain't the waves o' the sea," said Ben.

"She's a twister!" said Davy, pointing to the sky.

Sure enough, there was a cyclone headed straight for them. It was black as night, ugly as sin, and twice as sassy.

"You're a sailor, Ben," said Davy. "Let's steer this sail-buggy out o' here."

"You steer," said Ben Hardin. "I'll handle the sails."

Davy took his place at the wheel to steer, while Ben Hardin shinnied up the mast like a monkey. They both worked away, but that cyclone stayed right on their track. All the time the wind kept blowing, and the waves of the sea splashed high as little mountains. Thunder thundered, and lightning blasted all about.

Then Davy gave the wheel a quick twist, and they began to put some space between them and the cyclone.

"That did 'er!" said Davy.

The very next minute the cyclone rushed at them full steam ahead. It lashed out with its tail, knocking a hole smack-dab in the middle of the ship. The water poured in, and the ship began to make for the bottom of the sea.

"Ain't no twister goin' to sneak up on me that way!" said Davy, grabbing hold of the cyclone's tail. Ben Hardin grabbed hold too, and the whole kit and caboodle of them went flying across the sky.

"Good idee, Davy," said Ben Hardin. "This here beats ridin' a streak o' lightnin'."

"She don't steer as easy as lightnin'," said Davy. "Better hold tight, because this ain't goin' to be no hay ride."

Turned out that Davy was right. That cyclone kept twisting and lashing its tail, trying to shake them off. That didn't work, so it turned a somersault and did a few figure-eights. That didn't work either, so it took to spinning like a top. Then it gave up spinning and just tore across the sky, snorting more fearful than ever. It was going so fast they'd circled the earth twice before Davy figured out what was happening.

When he did catch on, he said, "She's makin' one round trip after another. Next time around, Ben, keep your good eye peeled for the United States. Sing out when you see 'er and we'll drop off."

Ben Hardin leaned way over, watching sharp. Soon as he saw the United States below he sang out, "United States below!"

Davy gave the cyclone's tail a yank to get it a little closer to earth.

"Comin' along, Ben?" said Davy.

"Might as well," said Ben Hardin.

And they both jumped, falling head over heels through the air. But they landed on top of a tree, so there was no harm done.

"Blast me boots if she ain't a palm tree," said Ben Hardin.

"This ain't no time to be jawin' about trees," said Davy. "I got to get back to Washington City and take care o' Slickerty Sam. Guess he'll be a mite surprised when he sees me sittin' up in Congress tomorrow mornin'."

"Hold on a minute, Davy," said Ben Hardin. "I don't think you'll be sittin' in Congress tomorrow mornin'. Don't think you'll be in Washington City a-tall. Because shiver me mizzen, if we ain't come down on an island o' the South Seas."

"Now, Ben," said Davy. "This ain't no time for tom-foolery."

"Ain't tom-foolin'," said Ben Hardin. "Have a look for yourself."

Davy had a look and saw that they were on a little bit of an island. There were palm trees growing, and bright-colored flowers, and a whole town of thatched grass hats.

"Why, you one-eyed walrus!" said Davy. "I told you to sing out when you saw the United States."

"That's exactly what I did do," said Davy.

"Then how come," roared Davy, "we ain't no place else but right here on an island o' the South Seas?"

CHAPTER TWENTY

BEN HARDIN DIDN'T ANSWER BACK A
word. He just looked sheepish-like, and started climbing
down the trunk of the palm tree. Davy followed along,
thinking things over in his head.

When he reached the ground, Davy said, "Ben, I've
got 'er figured out. That twister was goin' so fast, by the
time we dropped off we'd left the United States behind.
So you ain't to blame, and I'm sorry I lit into you the
way I did. Hope you won't have no hard feelin's."

"No hard feelin's a-tall, Davy," said Ben Hardin, cheering up a bit.

Before he'd been cheered up for long, a whole pack of South Sea folks came jumping out of the bushes. Those South Sea folks were black as Pennsylvania coal. They were all dressed in grass skirts and nothing much else besides. Every one of them carried a long spear, and they were howling and carrying on something fearful.

"Look out, Davy!" hollered Ben Hardin, rattling at the knees. "They're worse than red Injuns!"

"Don't you worry none," said Davy. "I never had no trouble with red Injuns, and I don't look for none with these folks here. I'll take care o' this."

The South Sea folks started pushing Davy and Ben Hardin away, giving them a jab with their spears to show they meant business. The next thing Davy and Ben Hardin knew they'd been hauled up in front of the Chief. The South Sea folks kept crowding around, jabbering away in South Sea language. Davy listened hard and he soon got the hang of it. Seemed the folks had never seen white men before. Half a dozen old grandpas standing near the Chief were saying a white man wasn't worth having around, and Davy and Ben ought to be killed off without any more fuss.

"Hold on there, Chief!" roared Davy in South Sea language. "For I'm Davy Crockett, Colonel in the army and Congressman from Tennessee in the United States! I'm half horse, half alligator, with a little touch o' snappin' turtle! Look out, for I'm a ring-tailed roarer, and I'm gettin' ready to roar!"

"Glad to meet you, Davy," said the Chief. "All the same, it won't do you no good to roar. You're a white man, and we got no use for 'em in these parts."

"Don't waste your time talkin', Chief," said the old grandpas. "Kill 'em off."

Ben Hardin got wind of what was going on and turned whiter than a clean sheet.

"Think o' somethin', Davy," he said. "And think of it fast."

"No need to worry," said Davy, and turned back to the Chief. "Looky here, Chief," he said, "down where I come from we don't kill off nobody without givin' them a trial. It wouldn't be fair and square."

"Don't listen to him, Chief!" yelled the grandpas. "He's just tryin' to talk his way out."

"Now wait a minute," said the Chief. "I can't have anybody sayin' I ain't fair and square. You go ahead and fix up a trial, Davy. I'll try anything once."

"Thank you, Chief," said Davy. He picked out twelve of the South Sea folks for the jury, got one old grandpa to be the lawyer against him, and asked the Chief to be judge.

"I'll be lawyer for myself and Ben Hardin," said Davy. After he'd told them all what they had to do, he said, "GO AHEAD!"

The old grandpas kept grumbling, but the Chief hushed them up.

"Order in this here court!" he hollered, just the way Davy had told him. "Now get on with the trial."

First one to talk was the old grandpa who was the lawyer against Davy.

"Gents o' the jury," he said, "this here trial is nothin' but a lot o' folderol. Ain't none o' us ever seen a white man before, but you only got to take one look to see they ain't like us. And if they ain't like us, they ain't worth a busted cocoanut, and they shouldn't ought to be kept alive. Our pas and grandpas never had no white

145

men on this here South Sea island—and what was good enough for them is good enough for us. Gents o' the jury, I'm askin' you to kill off Davy Crockett and Ben Hardin. That's all I got to say."

There was some cheering after that, especially among the grandpas. Ben Hardin shook so hard he almost trembled off his kneecaps.

"Shiver me mizzen, Davy," he said. "It looks like we're sunk for good."

Davy just gave him a laugh and started in talking.

"Gents o' the jury," he said, "I ain't goin' to make no long speech. I'm just goin' to tell you a little somethin' of how we do things back in the good old United States, where I come from. After that it'll be up to you to say if Ben and me ought to be killed off or not."

Then Davy didn't do anything but speak the Declaration of Independence and the Constitution of the United States. He knew it all by heart, the same as if he had it written down on paper. He went through it from beginning to end without skipping a single word. And when he got through, he said, "Any questions?"

"Just say that first part over again," said the Chief. "I kind o' like it."

Davy said the first part over again and asked once more, "Any questions?"

For a little while there wasn't a sound. Then the

South Sea folks let loose a cheer, with some of the old grandpas joining in.

"Order in this here court!" yelled the Chief. "Gents o' the jury, what have you got to say?"

"No two ways about it," said the jury. "Ain't any one man better than the next, no matter if he's black, white, or any which color. We ain't goin' to kill off Davy and Ben Hardin."

The folks let loose another cheer, hollering, "Hurrah for the jury! Hurrah for Davy! Hurrah for Ben Hardin!"

"What did I tell you, Ben?" said Davy. "I knew there couldn't nobody hold out against the Declaration o' Independence and the Constitution o' the United States."

While the cheering was still going on, the Chief called for a frolic. The South Seas folks began dancing, singing their own songs and beating out the time on drums. Davy and Ben Hardin danced beside them, doing everything from a reel to a square-toed double trouble shuffle. The South Sea folks were mighty pleased with their dancing. Even the old grandpas said it would have been a shame to kill off two steppers like that.

DIVING
for PEARLS

CHAPTER TWENTY-ONE

THE FROLIC KEPT UP TILL THE MIDDLE OF
the night, and Davy kept up with it. When it was over
he said to the Chief, "Had a fine time, Chief. But I
guess Ben and me had better be gettin' along. What's
the quickest way back to the good old United States?"
148

"Couldn't say," said the Chief, shaking his head. "The way I figure it, you're a long way from home. Ain't nothin' for miles around but blue sea water."

Ben Hardin was sitting alongside, and Davy asked him, "You're a sailor, Ben. How're we goin' to get home?"

"No way I know of," said Ben Hardin, "unless a ship comes along."

"Ain't no ships ever come by this way," said the Chief, shaking his head again.

"Well, o' course we could ride a streak o' lightnin'," said Davy. "Or hang on to the tail of a twister."

The Chief shook his head a third time.

"Don't have storms here but about once a year," he said. "And we just got through havin' one."

"Take my eyes for green grog bottles!" said Davy. "You mean to say there ain't no way o' gettin' off this here South Sea island and back to the good old United States?"

"Looks like it," said the Chief.

"Sure does," said Ben Hardin.

Davy stood up and walked over to the shore. A big moon was shining down on the waves of the sea, pretty as a picture. The sweet smell of flowers was in the air, and the South Sea varmints were making a buzz. But Davy didn't see any of it, or hear any of it, or smell any of it. For the first time since he'd left the Crockett cabin in Tennessee he felt like busting out crying like a baby.

He said, "What's goin' to become o' the good old United States without me there to run out Slickerty Sam? And how will I ever have my weddin' with Sally Ann?"

From that day on Davy didn't do a thing but stand on shore. He kept one eye on the waves of the sea, watching for a ship. He kept the other on the clouds of the sky, watching for lightning or a twister. The Chief tried to get him to join in a frolic or go diving with his boys, but Davy wouldn't hear of it. Besides watching, all he did was sigh and fret. It got so Ben Hardin began to worry over him.

"Ain't like Davy to be like this," said Ben Hardin, talking it over with the Chief. "He's gettin' to be no better than an old hulk on a lee shore. What with frettin' and sighin' and watchin', he's wastin' away to a shadow."

"Davy is a long ways off from bein' a shadow," said the Chief. "All the same, we got to do somethin' about it. I think I got an idee."

The Chief picked himself up and went over to Davy. "It sure beats all," said the Chief.

Davy didn't answer a word, but the Chief kept on.

"Yes, sir," said the Chief. "A man can be a big man at home, but when he gets somewheres else he don't amount to beans."

Still Davy didn't answer a word, and still the Chief kept on.

"Now you take divin'," said the Chief. "A man might be a mighty good river diver. But get him where there's nothin' but blue sea water, and he won't even wet his big toe. Well, I guess that's the way it's got to be."

"Then guess again!" roared Davy. "For you're talkin' about me, and I'm Davy Crockett! I can dive deeper, stay under water longer, and come up drier than any man before or since! What's more, I'll dive in river water, blue sea water, or the water of a deep-dug well!"

"Talkin' ain't divin'," said the Chief, quiet-like.

"Why, you South Seas hornswoggler!" bellowed Davy. "If I can't out-dive any man in this here neck o' the woods, I hope never to see the good old United States again! Call out your boys! I'll show 'em enough divin' to last 'em eighty-eight years!"

Soon as the Chief heard that, he let loose a yell. A dozen of his boys came running up, all ready to dive and saying so.

"Then GO AHEAD!" said Davy, jumping into the water. The Chief's boys followed after him, and they all went streaking down head first.

151

It wasn't long before Davy had left them out of sight. He kept diving ahead, not stopping till he reached bottom. Only trouble was, the darkness was so thick he couldn't see a thing.

"May as well have a look at the sights," said Davy, making a lampwick out of his hair and soaking it in elbow grease. He struck a spark by hitting his knuckles on a rock and lighted the lampwick.

Turned out that Davy was in the midst of thousands of oysters. Those oysters were giant oysters, and they were all asleep in their beds.

"If this ain't a breeze o' luck," said Davy, and he started in to sing:

> *Over the river to feed my sheep,*
> *Over the river to Charley,*
> *Over the river to feed my sheep,*
> *On buckwheat cakes and barley.*

The oysters stirred around a bit, and Davy sang out:

> *We're on our way to Baltimore,*
> *With two behind and two before,*
> *Around, around, around we go,*
> *Where oats, peas, beans and barley grow,*
> *In waiting for somebody.*

The oysters were so pleased they all opened up their shells for him. Inside of each was a pearl as big as a pumpkin. Davy picked up as many pearls as he could carry and swam up to the top of the water. The Chief's boys were all sitting around on shore, worn out with trying to dive as deep as Davy.

"Kind o' figured you wouldn't make it," said Davy, diving to the bottom again. He made ten more dives, bringing up a load of pearls each time.

He gave half of the pearls to the Chief, saying, "Pass 'em out among the folks. Compliments o' Davy Crockett."

Davy put the rest of the pearls in a sack, figuring they'd make a nice trinket for Sally Ann.

"Guess I was wrong," said the Chief. "A big man is a big man no matter where he's at. That is, if he's Davy Crockett."

But Davy didn't even hear the Chief, and he didn't perk up a bit. Once again he was standing on the shore, fretting and sighing. And once again he was watching the waves of the sea and the clouds of the sky.

CHAPTER TWENTY-TWO

BEN HARDIN AND THE CHIEF STARTED sighing along with Davy, the three of them making a sound like the wind in the trees. They'd been at it for an hour or more when Davy saw something out on the water.

"What's that floatin'?" said Davy.

"Could be a ship," said Ben Hardin.

"Could, but it ain't," said Davy. "Because it keeps slidin' under the water."

"Could be a shark," said the Chief.

"Could, but it ain't," said Davy. "It's too big."

The next minute the most monsteracious critter came into sight. It had green goggly eyes, teeth like boar's tusks, and scales shining like brass-work. It was a little like a sea fish, a little like a land snake, and a little like an alligator. It had a long slithering tail and was the size of a full-rigged ship.

"Well, shiver me mizzen," said Ben Hardin. "Why, I do believe—it might be—must be—couldn't be anythin' else—o' course it is—well, blast me boots if it ain't—"

"Might, could, is, and ain't what?" said Davy.

"Ain't nothin' else but the Cape Cod Sea Sarpint!" said Ben Hardin.

"Cape Cod is in New England, ain't it?" asked Davy.

"That's so," said Ben Hardin.

"Then let me at that there critter!" said Davy. "Because Slickerty Sam is a New England peddler, and there ain't nothin' good that ever come from there!"

"Batten down your hatch, Davy," said Ben Hardin. "Because New England lads is the best seamen that ever was, and this here Cape Cod Sea Sarpint is a special friend o' mine. There's lots o' good that's come out o' New England."

"Maybe," said Davy. "But I'd like to see it proved. O' course, if this here critter is a friend o' yours, that's different."

By that time the Sea Sarpint was close by to shore. It
reared up its head and hollered, "Ahoy, Ben Hardin!"
It had a voice like a herd of buffalo, but talked through
its nose like a New England man.

"Heave to, old shellback!" said Ben Hardin, and the
Sea Sarpint came closer. It churned the water with its
tail, winked one goggly eye, and sang out, "Thought
it was you, Ben! Ain't seen you since you left port in
a whaler."

"Glad to see you, old mossback!" said Ben Hardin. "This here is Davy Crockett."

"Not Colonel Crockett, Congressman o' the state o' Tennessee?" said the Sea Sarpint.

"Nobody else," said Davy.

"I've heard o' you, Davy," said the Sea Sarpint.

"And this here's the Chief o' this South Sea island," said Ben Hardin.

There were glad-to-meet-you's on all sides, and Ben

Hardin and the Sea Sarpint began jawing about old times. All the South Sea folks came up to have a peep at the Sea Sarpint, but the Chief sent them away. He said it wasn't polite to keep looking at a stranger.

"What are you doin' down this way," asked Ben Hardin.

"Just cruisin'," said the Sea Sarpint. "And I'll ask you the same."

Ben Hardin told the whole story, with Davy helping out.

"Lower me jib-sail!" said the Sea Sarpint. "Davy, you ain't got no more cause to watch and fret and sigh."

"How do you mean?" said Davy.

"I'm just on my way back to Cape Cod right now," said the Sea Sarpint. "I'd be pleased to have you hop on and come along. I'll drop you off in Washington City."

When Davy heard that, he took back everything he'd said about New England. He took it back double and let the Sea Sarpint know he did. Then he let out a whoop that had the palm trees shaking and began stepping out a reel. The Chief called out the folks, and soon they had a regular frolic going.

When the frolic was over Davy said his good-bys. He even said good-by to the grandpas, and *they* said they'd never forget his speech at the trial.

"Come around again," said the Chief.

"Glad to, if I can get away," said Davy. "Come over to Tennessee sometime if you ain't got nothin' else better to do."

Davy and Ben Hardin climbed on the back of the Sea Sarpint. The South Sea folks passed up Davy's sack of pearls and some baskets of fruit to eat on the way.

"All set, Ben?" asked Davy.

"All set," said Ben Hardin.

"Ready, Sea Sarpint?" asked Davy.

"Ready and anxious," said the Sea Sarpint.

"Then GO AHEAD!" said Davy.

The Sea Sarpint started swimming, going at a hurricane clip. In no time at all they'd left the island behind. Davy and Ben Hardin had nothing to do but sit back and ride.

After they'd been going awhile, the sky started to get gray. It kept on being gray, not getting lighter by day or darker by night. On top of that, the air got cold. And the closer they came to the good old United States, the colder it was. Davy thought it wasn't natural, but he was so glad to be getting back he didn't say a word. He didn't say a word even when they turned up the Potomac River and found it was frozen over.

"I'll take you right on up to Washington City," said the Sea Sarpint, sliding along on the ice.

"No need to trouble," said Davy.

"No trouble a-tall," said the Sea Sarpint. "Always did want to see the nation's capital."

They went on up the river, with Davy hardly able to wait to set foot on United States land again. Then the Sea Sarpint stopped, dropped its tail on shore, and Davy and Ben Hardin walked off as nice as you please.

Davy leaped into the air, kicked his heels together, and crowed like a rooster. He flapped his arms and he bellowed, "Look out, Slickerty Sam, for I'm back in these here United States! Look out, for I'm Davy Crockett, fresh from the South Seas! I'm half horse, half alligator, with a little touch o' snappin' turtle! I can wade the Mississippi, ride a streak o' lightnin', hold a bear too close for comfort, and whip my weight in wildcats! Look out, for I'm Congressman Crockett o' Tennessee, and I'm back in Washington City!"

He gave a whistle, and Death Hug, Mississip, and the dogs came running up. The dogs howled and wagged their tails, while Death Hug growled and Mississip boomed the bass of *Old Hundred*.

"I knew you'd be waitin' for my whistle," said Davy. And only then did he turn and take a good look around at Washington City in these here United States.

The BIG FREEZE

CHAPTER TWENTY-THREE

"WELL, I'LL BE SHOT!" SAID DAVY, FOR THE snow was piled up all about in drifts six feet high. The sky was as gray as a flannel blanket. The air was as cold as the edge of an ax. A mean wind was blowing, and there wasn't a leaf on a tree, or a soul in sight.

"Ben," said Davy, "what time o' year would you say she is?"

"Looks like December or thereabouts," said Ben Hardin.

"Looks like it, right enough," said the Sea Sarpint. "But the way I figure, she's the month o' May."

"I figure the same," said Davy. "The month o' May, and not far from June at that."

"She still looks like December," said Ben Hardin.

"Whatever she is or ain't, she's too cold for me," said the Sea Sarpint. "I'd best be leavin' before I shiver every last scale off my hide."

Davy shouldered his sack of pearls, not wanting to hold back the Sea Sarpint.

"I'd like to thank you for the trip," said Davy. "And I'll never say another word against New England as long as I live."

"Glad to hear it," said the Sea Sarpint, heaving himself around. "Good-by, Davy. See you in Cape Cod, Ben."

Davy waved good-by as the Sea Sarpint headed down the river, then started walking through the snow. Ben Hardin walked at his side, while Death Hug, Mississip, and the dogs followed behind.

Turning into Pennsylvania Avenue, they saw a stranger hurrying along. He was wrapped up so snug against the cold there wasn't anything of him showing but the eyes.

Davy gave him a how-do and asked, "Stranger, could you tell us the time o' year?"

"She's the month o' May," said the stranger, "and gettin' on for June. Won't be no summer a-tall if she keeps up like this. The country's sure goin' to rack and ruin with this here Big Freeze." He let loose a sigh all the way from the bottom of his boots and hurried on.

"Ben," said Davy, "there's somethin' wrong about a Big Freeze in the month o' May. And if Slickerty Sam ain't behind it, I'll eat a hickory stump, roots and all."

"What are you goin' to do?" asked Ben Hardin.

"Only one thing *to* do," said Davy. "I've got to see President Old Hickory Andy Jackson and find out what's been goin' on. I know I said me and Andy was on different sides o' the fence. But these here United States are in danger, and it ain't no time to be proud."

Davy left Ben Hardin behind with Death Hug, Mississip, and the dogs. He went straight to the White House, walked to the front door, and knocked. There wasn't any answer, so he raised his fist and knocked again.

After a while the door opened, and there stood Andy Jackson. He was the same Andy Jackson, and yet he wasn't the same. Because he wasn't standing straight and tall as a hickory tree. His back was bent over and his shoulders were hunched. His hair wasn't any more a blaze of red, but white as the snow all around. He

163

still had a nose like an eagle's and eyes like a hawk's, but now his nose kind of drooped and his eyes were tired.

"Davy Crockett," said Andy Jackson, quiet-like.

"Couldn't be nobody else," said Davy.

Andy Jackson stood there, looking at Davy as if he'd never seen him before. He looked Davy up and he looked Davy down, till it seemed he'd never be through looking. But at last he said, "Will you come in out o' the cold, Congressman Crockett?"

"Don't mind if I do, President Jackson," said Davy, following Andy Jackson inside to a room where a log fire burned in a fireplace.

In the glow of the fire Andy Jackson looked at Davy all over again. Neither one of them spoke a word, and the only sound was the crackle of the logs blazing away. Then Andy Jackson held out his hand and said, "Would you shake my hand, Congressman Crockett?"

"Glad to, President Jackson," said Davy, shaking Andy Jackson's hand.

And when Andy Jackson heard that, he stood straight and tall as a hickory tree. His eyes lit up like live coals, and he gave a wildcat screech. He and Davy circled around each other, crowing like roosters and flapping their arms.

"Why, you ol' slangwhanger!" said Andy Jackson.

"You ol' bushwhacker, you!" said Davy.

"You backwoods galumpus!" said Andy Jackson.

"You screechin' wildcat!" said Davy.

"You ring-tailed roarer!" said Andy Jackson.

"You ol' alligator!" said Davy.

"You ol' terrapin!" said Andy Jackson.

They busted out laughing, thumped each other on the back, and let loose a whoop that shook the White House.

"Never was so glad to see anybody in all my born days," said Andy Jackson. "Where've you been, Davy? Draw up a chair and tell me all about it."

Both of them sat down and Davy told what had happened.

"All my fault," said Andy Jackson. "Because I let loose my temper and didn't heed what you said about Slickerty Sam. I should 'have let you run him out o' the country."

"No use cryin' over spilt milk," said Davy. "I want to hear about this here Big Freeze."

"I'll begin at the beginnin'," said Andy Jackson, and he did.

Seemed that Slickerty Sam had started getting hold of land, just the way he'd told Davy. He'd got hold of Daybreak Hill and Peak o' Day, which was one of the highest places in Tennessee. It was so high that

165

standing on it you could see the wheels that made the sun and earth turn around.

"Well," said Andy Jackson, "it's been so cold this winter that at last the earth froze on its axis, and the sun froze, too."

"Burn my boots," said Davy. "That's why there wasn't any difference between day and night out at sea. That's why it kept gettin' colder and colder. I kind o' thought it wasn't natural."

"You ain't heard the worst," said Andy Jackson. "Only way to get the sun and earth rollin' is to climb the Peak o' Day. Now Slickerty Sam has been livin' there, but he won't lift a finger."

"The low-down varmint!" said Davy.

"That's just what I said," said Andy Jackson. "But you still ain't heard the worst. Slickerty Sam says the Peak o' Day is on his land, and he won't allow nobody to climb up it. Not unless we give him the whole state o' Tennessee, so's he can rent it out for cash money."

"I knowed it!" yelled Davy. "I knowed it! I knowed this here Big Freeze was Slickerty Sam's doin'! Why, the slitherin' rattlesnake! The cheatin' hornswoggler! The lyin', thievin', no good—"

"Just a minute, Davy," said Andy Jackson, holding up his hand. "You still ain't heard the worst yet. O' course·

I couldn't allow Slickerty Sam to get away with that, so I sent a regiment o' soldiers with orders to charge right up the hill. Trouble is, it's so cold out in the woods the soldiers just froze in their tracks. Thought I'd go myself, but Congress won't let me. They say how do they know I won't freeze in *my* tracks, and they can't allow that to happen to no president o' the United States."

Davy jumped up from his chair, his eyes shooting white fire like lightning before a gust breaks out.

"That settles it," he said. "I'm startin' out for Tennessee right now. I'll take care o' Slickerty Sam, get the sun and earth rollin', and end this here Big Freeze. I got to, or else the whole country will go to ruin."

"Hold on there!" said Andy Jackson. "Suppose you get froze in your tracks?"

"Never was a freeze that could freeze me," said Davy.

"You're forgettin' she's a mighty freeze," said Andy Jackson.

"You're forgettin' I'm Davy Crockett," said Davy. "Looky here, Andy, you ain't tryin' to keep me back, are you?"

"Didn't think I could," said Andy Jackson. "But there's one more thing. This here Big Freeze is gettin' worse every minute. Ain't there some way you could get the sun shinin' first and take care o' Slickerty Sam afterwards?"

"I could set a trap," said Davy.

"What kind o' trap?" asked Andy Jackson. "What'll you use for bait?"

"Got just the right thing," said Davy, chuckling. "I brought back some pearls from the South Seas, every one as big as a punkin. I'll strew 'em around where Slickerty Sam can see 'em. Soon as he starts pickin' 'em up, I'll scoot up the hill. By the time he's pickin' up the last one, I'll be back down again."

"Go to it, you ol' rip-snorter!" said Andy Jackson, laughing and whacking Davy on the back.

"Just one more thing," said Davy. "Got a pair o' ice skates handy?"

"Must be some around somewheres," said Andy Jackson.

He went up to the attic, rooted around a bit, and came back with a pair of ice skates.

"Found an old pair that belonged to Tom Jefferson," he said. He gave them to Davy, and together they walked to the front door.

"Take care o' yourself, Davy," said Andy Jackson.

"Take care o' your own self," said Davy. "Because Davy Crockett's goin' to end this here Big Freeze."

THAWING OUT

CHAPTER TWENTY-FOUR

FIRST THING DAVY DID WAS STOP AT THE
Capitol Building and get old Betsy out of the cloakroom. After that he went to where Ben Hardin was
waiting with Death Hug, Mississip, and the dogs. He
told Ben Hardin what was going on and what he aimed
to do. He told Death Hug, Mississip, and the dogs he
was leaving them behind, but to come running when

169

he whistled. Then Davy put on the ice skates, and picked up old Betsy and his sack of pearls.

"See you in Tennessee," he said, and started skating.

Davy was a regular rocket on skates, and he went along faster than a streak of lightning set up edgeways and buttered with quicksilver. It wasn't but a minute till he was out of Washington City and sliding across the frozen Potomac River. He got up enough speed in Virginia to carry him over the mountains, then skated down into the state of Tennessee.

All the time it was getting colder and colder. The wind howled meaner than ever, but the trees were frozen so stiff they didn't move a branch. The sky kept turning darker shades of gray, and the snowdrifts kept getting deeper. There weren't any folks to be seen, or critters either. The folks stayed inside their cabins, and the critters had burrowed into the ground.

Davy skated along, going up hill, down hill, and on the level. Getting closer to Daybreak Hill, he saw the regiment of soldiers Andy Jackson had sent. They were all frozen in their tracks, standing just the way they'd been marching.

"Poor fellers," said Davy, dropping a tear that turned to an icicle before it hit the ground.

He thought he'd build a fire to thaw them out a bit.

But his tinder box would no more catch fire than a raft at the bottom of the sea. He tried to strike a spark from his fingers, and brought his knuckles together like thunderclouds. But the sparks froze up before he could collect them.

"Well, don't you worry none," said Davy to the soldiers. "You'll thaw out proper when the sun starts shinin' and be good as new."

Davy skated along again, going as fast as thought. A couple of times he skinned a tree, peeling off a piece of the bark. Still he kept skating on, and at last he came to Daybreak Hill with the Peak o' Day rising on top of it. There was a picket fence to keep folks off and signs that said:

SLICKERTY SAM'S LAND
KEEP OFF!
THIS MEANS YOU

"We'll see about that," said Davy. He skated around Daybreak Hill in a great circle, dropping pearls from his sack.

After he'd dropped them all, he hid behind a snowdrift, took off his skates, and watched. It wasn't long before Slickerty Sam came out of his cabin. He kept changing himself to a peddler, a gambling man, and a bully of the river—one right after the other. Whenever he got cold he changed himself from one to the next and was warm all over again.

Slickerty Sam snooped around to see if anybody was on his land. Then he stopped, catching sight of the pearls. He walked down to the picket fence, had a good look, and shook his head.

"Nope," he said. "There ain't no such pearls. Couldn't be. Never was and never will be."

He scratched his chin and thought it over for a minute.

"And if there was such pearls," he said, "how'd they get here anyways?"

He tried walking away from the picket fence, but he couldn't. He turned and walked right back again. He looked at the pearls nestling in the snow, each one of them a beauty.

"It's a trick, ain't it?" he said.

Of course there wasn't any answer.

"Well, what if it is?" he said, answering himself. "Guess it won't do no harm to pick 'em up."

He hopped over the fence and began picking up the pearls. Quick as a flash, Davy hopped over the fence and started up Daybreak Hill.

The cold was at its coldest, but Davy walked at a frolic gait, singing *Fire in the Mountain* in three double-quick time. He didn't stop at all till he was up Daybreak

Hill and on the Peak o' Day. Standing right at the edge, he saw the wheels and cogwheels and the rest of the gear for making the sun and earth go around. The earth was frozen on its axis, just as he'd been told. The sun had got jammed between two cakes of ice under the wheels. There it had been shining and working to get loose, until it had frozen fast in its own sweat.

"C-r-e-a-t-i-o-n!" said Davy. "I've got to get things rollin', and rollin' fast, or human creation is done for."

Davy went back a piece among the rocks, searching

for a cave. When he found one he let loose a fearful howl.

"If there's a bear asleep in the cave," he said, "that howl should fetch him."

Sure enough, a bear came tearing out. Davy pulled the trigger of old Betsy, and that's all there was to it. He picked up the bear, went to the top again, and squeezed the bear over the earth's axis. Hot, sweet bear oil poured all over, and soon the earth's axis began to

thaw loose. Davy kept squeezing, pouring a ton or more of the oil over the sun's face. He gave the earth's cog-wheel a kick backward till the sun got free and whistled *Push Along, Keep Moving*.

In about fifteen seconds the earth gave a grunt and began to roll around easy. The sun walked up most beautiful, saluting Davy with such a wind of gratitude it made him sneeze. Davy lit his pipe by the sun's top-knot, put a piece of sunrise in his pocket, and started back down.

As Davy walked off the Peak o' Day down Daybreak Hill, the sun rose up behind him. The air got warmer, the ice started to melt, and the snow to thaw. Instead of a mean wind a fresh breeze blew, shaking the trees soft and gentle. Birds flew out, twittering sweet music, while the critters and varmits began to stir.

"Right pretty mornin' after all," said Davy. "Now to take care o' Slickerty Sam."

When Davy got to the bottom of the hill, Slickerty Sam was picking up the last of the pearls.

"Just like I figured," said Davy. He leaped into the air, kicked his heels together, and neighed like a horse. He flapped his arms, crowed like a rooster, and he bellowed, "Look out, Slickerty Sam! For I'm Davy Crockett, the yaller blossom o' the forest. I'm half horse, half alligator, with a little touch o' snappin' turtle! I'm a Colonel o' the army, a Congressman o' Tennessee, and the greatest hunter that ever was! I can ride a streak o' lightnin', look a panther to death, hold a buffalo out to drink, and lick my weight in wildcats! Look out, Slickerty Sam, for I'm Davy Crockett and I mean to lay you low!"

BE SURE YOU'RE RIGHT
THEN
GO AHEAD

CHAPTER TWENTY-FIVE

WHEN SLICKERTY SAM HEARD THAT, HE
didn't even look up.

"Davy Crockett!" he said, dropping all the pearls.

He jumped one jump, howled one howl, and lit out
fast. Like a bear after sweet honey, he headed straight
for the Mississippi River. It was still frozen over and he

slid along on the ice, trying to put space between him and Davy.

Then the sun gave a great shine and the river started in to thaw. The ice cracked, and the chunks floated down stream in a rush.

Davy had been chasing after Slickerty Sam, but now he stopped at the river's edge.

"Well, saw me into weatherboards!" he said. For if Davy had ever seen a man down-right, up-right, and every which way surprised, that man was Slickerty Sam. He was sitting on a chunk of ice, his jaw hanging and his eyes popping. He let out a yelp now and then, but there wasn't anything he could do but keep floating down the river. The way the water was rushing he'd be carried out to sea, just the way he'd done to Davy.

"Keep on travelin'!" roared Davy. "And don't you ever set foot on these here United States again! If you do I'll lay you low, sure as my name is Davy Crockett!"

Davy followed along shore for a while, singing loud so that Slickerty Sam could hear him:

> Met Mr. Catfish comin' down stream,
> Says Mr. Catfish, "What does you mean?"
> Caught Mr. Catfish by the snout,
> And turned Mr. Catfish right side out.

When Slickerty Sam had floated out of sight, Davy whistled for Death Hug, Mississip, and the dogs. He put the pearls back in the sack, turned and started walking again. By this time the sun had risen full up, and the thaw was going on proper. As Davy stepped along, flowers sprang up in his path. Greenery started to show all about, and streams of water to flow. The forest trees burst into bud, with birds flying and twittering from the branches. There was a rustle and bustle everywhere, while the critters and varmints walked out on all sides. To top it off, a little wind blew, whispering, "Davy Crockett . . . Davy Crockett . . . Davy Crockett. . . ."

Davy breathed in the sweet air and smiled.

"She's a nice mornin' for certain," he said.

Going on a piece, he came to the regiment of soldiers Andy Jackson had sent. They'd thawed out good as new, and now they were lined up ready to march. They gave Davy a salute, their brass buttons and swords flashing in the sunlight.

"What are your orders, Colonel Crockett?" asked the captain.

"If you've got nothin' else to do," said Davy, "you might spread the word around that Davy Crockett is havin' his weddin' with Sally Ann Thunder Ann Whirlwind, and all comers are welcome. When you get through doin' it, come over yourselves."

"Yes, sir, Colonel Crockett," said the captain, and the soldiers marched off to spread the word.

179

Davy went on again till he came to the cabin of Sally Ann's Pa next to Asphaltum Flats. Sally Ann was standing in front of the cabin, her yellow hair as smooth as cornsilk and her eyes blue as periwinkles.

"Glad you're back, Davy," she said.

"Glad to *be* back," said Davy. "Got a little trinket for you," he said, handing her the pearls.

"Thank you, Davy," said Sally Ann. "Right pretty, ain't they?"

Then Sally Ann's Pa came out of the cabin.

"Enough o' this jawin'!" he said. "What about the weddin'?"

"Well," said Davy, giving Sally Ann a wink, "I should be gettin' back to Congress and finish out my term." Sally Ann's Pa opened his mouth to holler, but Davy said, "Come to think o' it, I guess I could go back afterwards."

"Now you're talkin'!" said Sally Ann's Pa, and they began to get ready for the wedding.

Sally Ann's Pa rounded up some of the folks thereabouts to help. The men folks brought axes and helped Davy chop logs for tables and benches. The women folks brought skillets and stew pans and helped Sally Ann cook for the feast. All the while Davy kept cutting up, while Sally Ann giggled worse than a chicken clucking.

A couple of days before the wedding, Death Hug, Mississip, and the dogs came running up. Davy went out to the woods, hunting all sorts of critters so there'd be meat for the feast. When he came back he found Ben Hardin had blown in.

"Ahoy, Davy!" said Ben Hardin. "How about startin' the frolic? I'm just itchin' to dance."

"There'll be dancin' a-plenty," said Davy. "But now you pitch in and help."

The next day Davy's Ma and Pa, his Uncle Roarious and his Aunt Ketinah showed up.

"He's lookin' frisky," said Davy's Ma.

"Looks strong, too," said Davy's Pa.

"I'm strong as they come and frisky as a wildcat," said Davy.

"He's still quirky," said Uncle Roarious.

"Still full o' sass," said Aunt Ketinah.

"Yes, ma'am," said Davy, always polite to the ladies.

Soon the folks began drifting in thick and fast. There was Uncle Zebulon from Old Kaintuck, riding horseback with his Thunder and Lightning Screamers. There was the Indian tribe Davy was a member of, led by the Chief. There was a whole slue of Sally Ann's uncles, cousins, and aunts, and of course the preacher. And on the day of the wedding the soldiers came marching in, and with them was Andy Jackson.

181

"Told you I'd end the Big Freeze," said Davy.

"Knew you would," said Andy Jackson. "What about Slickerty Sam?"

"Slickerty Sam?" said Davy, giving a chuckle. "Why, the last I saw o' him he was headed for sea, sittin' on a chunk o' ice."

"Guess he was kind o' surprised," said Andy Jackson.

"Well, he did look a mite put out," said Davy. "O' course he couldn't have looked any other way. Because he *was* put out—clear out o' these here United States."

They both busted out laughing and circled around each other, screeching and crowing the way they always did.

"Enough o' this carryin' on," said Sally Ann's Pa. "Let's start the weddin'!"

The wedding went off as a wedding should, with Andy Jackson as best man and Ben Hardin as second best. Sally Ann's Pa gave away the bride, the preacher did his part, then there was kissing and handshaking all around. After that they went to Asphaltum Flats, where the tables had been spread for the feast.

They hadn't been feasting for more than three or four hours when Sally Ann's Pa got up and whipped out his hemlock fiddle. He started playing away and singing:

Turkey in the straw, turkey in the hay,
Roll 'em up and twist 'em up a high tuckahaw,
And hit 'em up a tune called Turkey in the Straw.

Some other folks picked up banjos, guitars, more fiddles, and clarinets. The way they hit up the tune was a treat.

"Choose partners and form the set!" called Sally Ann's Pa, and the frolic was on.

In no time at all the folks were dancing, shaking Asphaltum Flats like an earthquake. Davy and Sally Ann stepped as they'd never stepped before, and so did Ben Hardin. All the Crocketts joined in, and Sally Ann's uncles, cousins, and aunts, as well as the Indians and the soldiers. Andy Jackson stamped it out with the rest, his coat tails flying. The Indians hollered Indian yells, the soldiers shot off their pistols, and there was whooping, laughing, and singing by one and all.

"Swing your partner!" called Sally Ann's Pa. "Cut the figure eight! Dos a dos!"

The sky arched high overhead, and the sun shone splendiferously. After the sun went down the moon came up, twice as big as natural. There was hardly any need for the pitchpine torches the folks had lit.

Along about the third day of the frolic, Davy and Sally Ann were dancing something furious. They'd just gone into a square-toed double trouble shuffle, when a man on horseback rode up and spoke to Andy Jackson.

"What's up, Andy," asked Davy, still dancing.

"It's Slickerty Sam again," said Andy Jackson.

"Slickerty Sam!" said Davy, and this time he didn't chuckle. He left off dancing, and so did the rest of the folks. The music stopped, and everyone crowded around.

"Seems that Slickerty Sam got back to land," said Andy Jackson, "and now he's stirrin' up a war in Texas. Says he's goin' to own it all and rent it out for cash money—and she never will be one o' these here United States."

Davy looked around at all the folks. He looked at Ben Hardin in his tarpaulin hat and sailcloth trousers. He looked at the Indian Chief, at his Ma and Pa, his Aunt Ketinah and his Uncle Roarious. He looked at Andy Jackson, standing straight and tall as a hickory tree. He looked at Sally Ann's Pa, and at Sally Ann, with her yellow hair like cornsilk and her eyes blue as periwinkles.

"She's a long way to the Texas," said Davy's Pa.

"You ain't even finished your weddin' frolic," said Davy's Ma.

"I know it's a long way to the Texas," said Davy. "I know I ain't finished my weddin' frolic. But I ain't finished off Slickerty Sam like I said I would, and that's what I've got to do."

"Davy," said Sally Ann, "are you sure you're right?"

"I am," said Davy.

"Then GO AHEAD!" said Sally Ann.

"That's what I aim to do," said Davy, picking up old Betsy. He whistled to Death Hug, Mississip, and the dogs, and he said his good-bys. It took a while for him to say good-by to all the folks, but at last he was through.

"Guess I'd better be goin'," said Davy.

"We'll walk along with you a ways," said Andy Jackson.

In the last light of the setting sun, the folks walked along with Davy. Somebody started in to sing *Fare You Well, Traveler*, and soon all the folks were singing:

> *Fare you well, traveler,*
> *Fare you well a while,*
> *You'll travel many a weary mile.*
> *It's a long way from home*
> *If to the Texas you must roam,*
> *So fare you well, fare you well a while.*
>
> *Fare you well, traveler,*
> *Fare you well a while,*
> *You'll travel many a lonely mile.*
> *You have left behind your bride*
> *And have no one by your side,*
> *So fare you well, fare you well a while.*

At the edge of Asphaltum Flats the folks stopped, but Andy Jackson walked on with Davy.

"You can still turn back, Davy," said Andy Jackson.

"No," said Davy, "I couldn't do that. She's a mighty

fine country, these here United States, and we can't allow anybody like Slickerty Sam to ruin it. I've got to take care o' him, just like I said, and I couldn't turn back if I wanted to."

"Didn't think you could, you ring-tailed roarer!" said Andy Jackson. "Now GO AHEAD, and let 'em hear your roar in Texas!"

And when Andy Jackson said that, stars flashed in the blue of the sky. The northern lights rippled out in red and white stripes, and there was a roll of thunder like the rumble of drums.

"So long, Andy," said Davy, and he leaped on Death Hug. Then he streaked out for the Texas, with Mississip and the dogs streaking along behind.

AND THATS NOT ALL

Now some folks say Davy Crockett was killed at the Alamo, fighting for Texas. Well, what some folks don't know would fill a book. The folks that *do* know say that Davy kept fighting until Slickerty Sam was run out of the country and Texas was made one of these here United States. They say Davy was seen afterwards hunting buffalo on the prairies, and he was seen in Arkansas, Tennessee, and Old Kaintuck.

And they say that someday you'll be walking along,

when you'll hear a howling and a barking. You'll turn around and you'll see some hunting dogs, named Whirlwind, Old Rattler, Soundwell, Tiger, Growler, Holdfast, Grim, Deathmaul, and Thunderbolt. Those will be Davy's dogs.

Then you'll hear a bass voice singing out *Old Hundred,* and you'll see a buffalo—that'll be Mississip. You'll hear a grunt and a growl, and you'll see a bear standing on his hind legs. That'll be Death Hug.

After that you'll hear a crow like a rooster, a neigh like a horse, and voice roaring, "Look out, for I'm Davy Crockett, the yaller blossom o' the forest! I'm half horse, half alligator, with a little touch o' snappin' turtle! I can wade the Mississippi, ride a streak o' lightnin', hug a bear too close for comfort, and whip my weight in wildcats! I can fight fisstiferously, kick hossiferously, and howl wolfiferously! I can out-eat, out-sleep, out-fight, out-shoot, run faster, jump higher, squat lower, dive deeper, stay under water longer and come up drier than

any man in these here United States! Look out, because I'm a ring-tailed roarer, and this is my day to roar! W-h-o-o-o-o-o-o-o-p!"

The wind will howl riproariously. The trees will shiver and shake. Thunder will boom, and all the critters and varmints of the forest will let out a moan.

Then you'll see a man dressed in a coonskin cap, a fringed buckskin shirt, buckskin breeches, and moccasins. He'll have a rifle in his hand by the name of old Betsy, and maybe a piece of sunrise in his pocket.

"Mornin', stranger," he'll say. "She's a right pretty country, ain't she? Always thought so and always will."

And that will be Davy Crockett, still around to keep Slickerty Sam out of these here United States.